ORIGO
STEPPING STONES

CORE MATHEMATICS

SENIOR AUTHORS

James Burnett

Calvin Irons

PROGRAM CONSULTANTS

Diana Lambdin

Frank Lester, Jr.

Kit Norris

CONTRIBUTING AUTHORS

Debi DePaul

Peter Stowasser

Allan Turton

PROGRAM EDITORS

James Burnett

Beth Lewis

Donna Richards

EDUCATION

STUDENT JOURNAL

CONTENTS

The *ORIGO Stepping Stones* program has been created to provide a smarter way to teach and learn mathematics. It has been developed by a team of experts to provide a world-class math program.

STUDENT JOURNAL

Engaging student pages accompany each lesson within *ORIGO Stepping Stones*. In the Student Journals for Grades 1–5, there are two pages for each lesson. Following are the features of the Grade 5 Student Journal as a part of the whole program.

STEP 1

Step 1 provides guided discussion of enquiry. This often sets the scene for the lesson. Teachers can project this piece of the lesson and step through each question or point one at a time.

STEP 2

Step 2 provides individual work based on the discussion above.

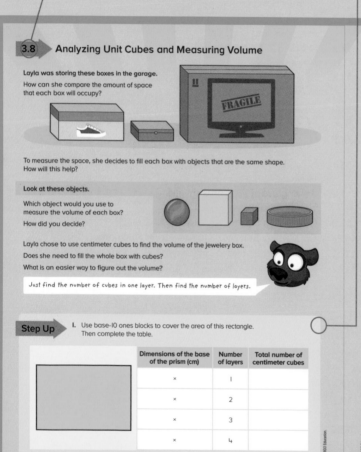

STEP 3

Step 3 puts a little twist on each lesson to develop higher-order thinking skills.

ORIGO Stepping Stones 5 • 3.8

Grade   Module   Lesson

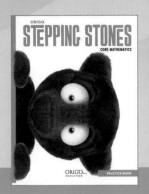

PRACTICE BOOK

Regular and meaningful practice is a hallmark of *ORIGO Stepping Stones*. Each module in this book has perforated pages that practice content previously learned to maintain concepts and skills, and pages that practice computation to promote fluency.

NOTES FOR HOME

Each book is one component of a comprehensive teaching program. Together they are a collection of consolidation and practice pages from lessons in the *ORIGO Stepping Stones* program.

Class teachers will decide which pages suit individual needs. So students might not complete every page in these books. For more information about the program, visit **www.origoeducation.com/steppingstones**.

ADDITIONAL RESOURCES — PRINT

The Number Case provides teachers with ready-made resources that are designed to develop students' understanding of number.

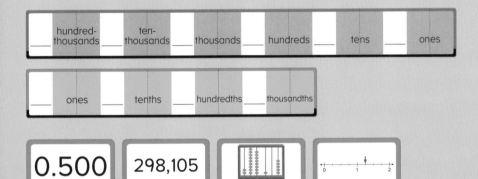

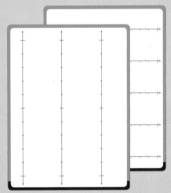

ADDITIONAL RESOURCES (ONLINE CHANNELS)

These are some of the innovative teaching channels integrated into the teacher's online program.

ORIGO MathEd

Professional learning sessions

Flare

Interactive whiteboard tools

Fundamentals Game Boards

Interactive games

ALGORITHM

Algorithms are rules used for completing tasks or for solving problems. There are standard algorithms for calculating answers to addition, subtraction, multiplication and division problems.

For example:

```
              2   0   8
        _____
     4 ) 8    3   2
        - 8   ↓   ↓
          0   3   2
            - 3   2
                  0
```

AREA

Area is the amount of surface that a shape covers. This amount is usually described in square units such as square centimeters (cm²) or square inches (in²).

COMMON DENOMINATORS

To compare, add, or subtract two or more common fractions with related or different denominators, equivalent fractions are used so that all the fractions have **common denominators**.

For example, see $\frac{2}{3} + \frac{3}{4}$ and change both fractions to show common denominators: $\frac{8}{12} + \frac{9}{12}$.

COORDINATE PLANE

A **coordinate plane** is a rectangular grid which has a horizontal axis called the x-axis and a vertical axis called the y-axis. The origin is where the axes meet.

An **ordered pair** is two numbers that describe a specific point on a coordinate plane. These numbers are called coordinates. Marking ordered pairs on a coordinate plane is called graphing or plotting.

DECIMAL FRACTION

Decimal fractions are fractions in which the denominator is 10, 100, or 1,000, etc. but are always written using decimal points.

For example: $\frac{3}{10}$ can be written as 0.3 and $\frac{28}{100}$ can be written as 0.28

DECIMAL POINT

A **decimal point** indicates which digit is in the ones place. It is positioned immediately to the right of the ones digit. For example, in this numeral, 3 is in the ones place.

23.85

A digit's **decimal place** is its position on the right-hand side of the decimal point. The first decimal place to the right of the decimal point is the tenths place. The next place is called hundredths. For example, in the numeral 23.85, 8 is in first decimal place so is called 8 tenths.

EQUIVALENT FRACTIONS

Equivalent fractions are fractions that cover the same amount of area on a shape or are located on the same point on a number line.

For example: $\frac{1}{2}$ is equivalent to $\frac{2}{4}$

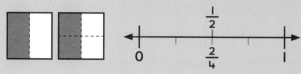

EXPONENTIAL NOTATION

Exponential notation is often used to represent very large numbers. It involves repeatedly multiplying a base number. The diagram shows that 10^3 is equivalent to $10 \times 10 \times 10$, so $10^3 = 1,000$.

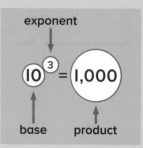

FACTORS

Factors are whole numbers that evenly divide another whole number. For example, 4 and 5 are both factors of 20 and 20 is a multiple of both 4 and 5.

FRACTION

In a common fraction (for example, $\frac{2}{3}$) the **denominator** shows the number of equal parts (3) in the whole, and the **numerator** shows the number of those parts (2) being considered.

IMPROPER FRACTIONS

Improper fractions are common fractions that have a numerator that is greater than or equal to the denominator. For example, $\frac{7}{5}$ is an improper fraction.

A **mixed number** is an improper fraction that has been changed to show the whole part/s and the fractional part. For example, $\frac{13}{6}$ is the same as $2\frac{1}{6}$.

LENGTH

Customary Units of Length		Metric Units of Length	
12 inches	I foot	10 millimeters	I centimeter
3 feet	I yard	100 centimeters	I meter
1,760 yards	I mile	1,000 meters	I kilometer

LINE PLOT

A **line plot** is used to show data. It is made by placing dots above a number line. On this line plot, each dot represents one student.

Number of Skips in I Minute – a Grade 5 Class

			●								
			●	●							
			●	●	●						
	●		●	●	●						
	●		●	●	●	●	●				
●	●	●	●	●	●	●	●	●	●	●	●
40	41	42	43	44	45	46	47	48	49	50	51

LIQUID VOLUME (CAPACITY)

Customary Units of Liquid Volume		Metric Units of Liquid Volume	
8 fluid ounces	I cup	1,000 milliliters	I liter
2 cups	I pint	1,000 liters	I kiloliter
2 pints	I quart		
4 quarts	I gallon		

MASS (WEIGHT)

Customary Units of Mass		Metric Units of Mass	
16 ounces	I pound	1,000 grams	I kilogram

ORDER OF OPERATIONS

If there is one type of **operation** in a sentence, work left to right. If there is more than one type of operation, work left to right in this order:

1. perform any operation inside parentheses
2. calculate any products of base numbers and exponents (exponentiation)
3. multiply or divide pairs of numbers
4. add or subtract pairs of numbers.

PARALLELOGRAM

A **parallelogram** is a quadrilateral with exactly two pairs of parallel sides.

PERIMETER

A **perimeter** is the boundary of a shape and the total length of that boundary.

For example, the perimeter of this rectangle is 20 inches.

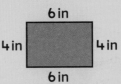

TRIANGLE

A **scalene triangle** has no sides that are equal in length and no angles equal in size.

An **isosceles triangle** has at least two sides of equal length and at least two angles equal in size.

An **equilateral triangle** has three sides of equal length and three angles equal in size.

VOLUME

Volume is the amount of space that an object occupies. This amount is usually described in cubic units such as cubic centimeters (cm^3) or cubic inches (in^3).

What number is represented on this abacus?

Draw one more bead on the ten thousands rod.

Write the new number. _____

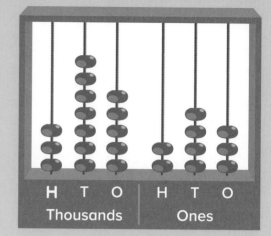

Write the new number in words.

_____

_____

Look at this abacus.
Draw a red bead on one of the rods to the left of the green bead.

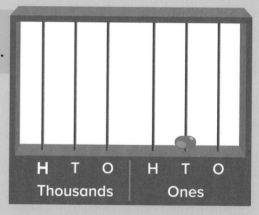

How can you describe the relationship between the red and green beads?

Step Up ▶

1. Draw beads on each abacus to represent the number.

a.   431,573

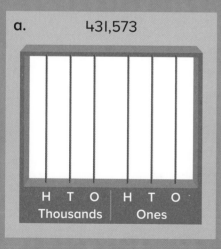

b.   703,258

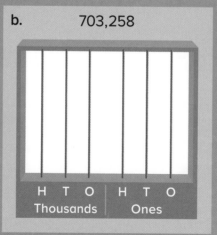

c.   190,640

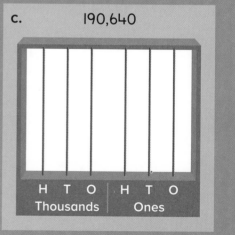

2. Complete the missing parts.

a.

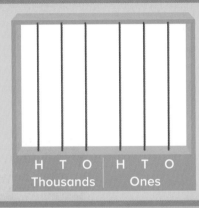

four hundred ninety-six
thousand seventy

b.

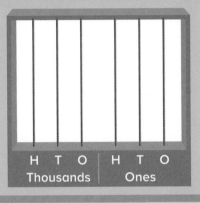

285,905

c.

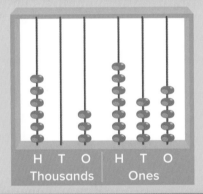

3. Write the numeral to match each number name.

a. Two hundred forty-six thousand one hundred fifty-two

b. One hundred seventy thousand one hundred seven

Step Ahead Color the ⬭ beside the expression that represents 503,851.

- ⬭ 5,000 + 300 + 80 + 50 + 1
- ⬭ 500,000 + 30,000 + 800 + 50 + 1
- ⬭ 500,000 + 3,000 + 800 + 50 + 1
- ⬭ 50,000 + 3,000 + 800 + 50 + 1

Building a Picture of One Million

Imagine you start at 1,000 and skip count by 1,000.

What number will you say after 999,000?

1,000 ... 2,000
3,000 ... 4,000...

Look carefully at the place-value chart below.
What place names belong in the three spaces
below **Millions**?
What abbreviations would you write?

Millions			Thousands			Ones		
			H	T	O	H	T	O

How many thousands are
there in one million?

Write numbers in the chart to show one million.

How could you represent one million using different base-10 blocks?
How do you know?

Exponential notation is often used to represent very
large numbers. It involves repeatedly multiplying a
base number. The diagram on the right shows that
10^3 is equivalent to $10 \times 10 \times 10$, so $10^3 = 1,000$.

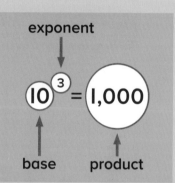

exponent

$10^3 = 1,000$

base   product

Look at the picture below.

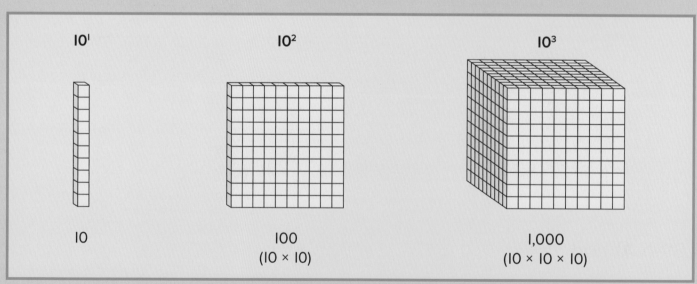

10^1

10^2

10^3

10

100
(10×10)

1,000
($10 \times 10 \times 10$)

What patterns do you see?
How could you represent 10^4? What would you write?

1. Imagine you had blocks of each size. Write the missing numbers. Then write a matching equation.

A **millions** block could be traded for

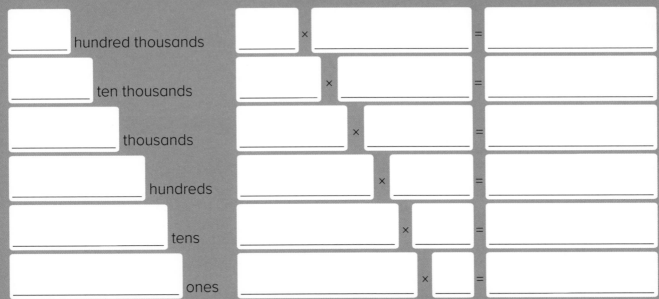

_____ hundred thousands

_____ ten thousands

_____ thousands

_____ hundreds

_____ tens

_____ ones

2. Write an expression to explain what each of these means.

a. 10^6 _____

b. 10^5 _____

3. Draw lines to connect matching values. Not every value has a match.

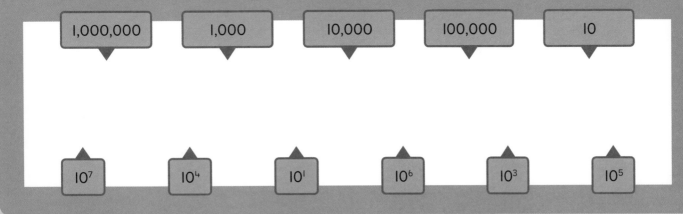

| 1,000,000 | 1,000 | 10,000 | 100,000 | 10 |

| 10^7 | 10^4 | 10^1 | 10^6 | 10^3 | 10^5 |

Scientists often use exponential notation to work with very large or very small numbers. For example, 3,000 may be written as 3×10^3. Write each of these numbers using exponential notation.

a. $400 = 4 \times$ _____

b. $60,000 =$ _____

c. $5,000,000 =$ _____

Reading and Writing Seven-Digit Numbers

What place-value names are said when you say a seven-digit number?

How would you say the number on this expander?

Read this number.

five million four hundred twenty thousand two hundred eighteen

Write it on this expander.

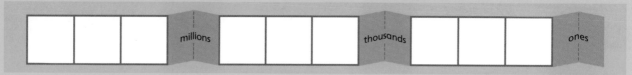

How did you know where to write each digit? How did you know where to write the zeros?

Zeros are written when there is no value in a place.

Step Up   1. Read the number name. Then write the matching number on each expander.

a. one million seven hundred fifteen thousand twenty-nine

b. four million three hundred eighty thousand two hundred one

2. Write the matching number on each expander.

a. seven million fifty-six thousand nine hundred thirty

			millions				thousands				ones

b. five million one hundred eight thousand five

			millions				thousands				ones

c. six million six thousand four hundred eighty-eight

			millions				thousands				ones

3. Read the number. Then write the matching numeral.

a. two million eight hundred three thousand _____

b. five million eight hundred thirty-three thousand four hundred two _____

c. one million eighteen thousand three hundred forty-two _____

d. nine million eighty-three thousand four hundred twenty _____

Step Ahead

Read the number on the expander.
Then write in words the number that is **10 thousand greater**.

		5	millions	2	0	8	thousands	6	1	5	ones

_____

_____

_____

1.4 ▶ Locating Large Numbers on a Number Line

This poster was used to show the total funds raised to help build a new wing at a hospital.

What amount was raised?

What does each mark on the poster represent?

What amount is each month showing? How do you know?

How can you figure out the increase in the amount raised from one arrow to the next on the poster?

Where do you think September might be located? How did you decide?

How could you use the marks to help you locate each of these amounts?

$1,290,000	$1,920,000	$920,000
$810,000	$180,000	$1,180,000

$1,290,000 is just a little less than the third mark above $1,000,000.

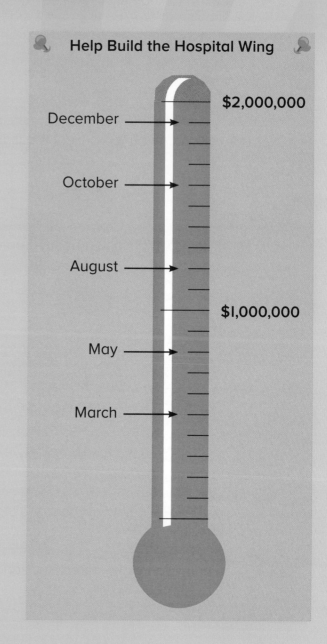

Help Build the Hospital Wing

- December → $2,000,000
- October →
- August →
- $1,000,000
- May →
- March →

Step Up ▶ For Questions 1 to 4, write the number shown by each arrow.

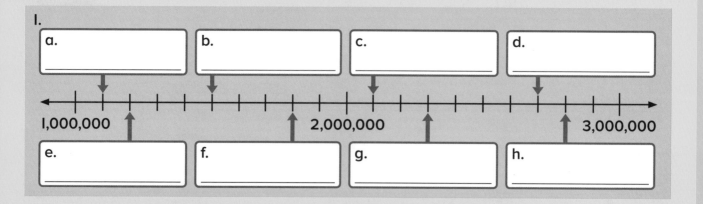

1.

a. _____ b. _____ c. _____ d. _____

1,000,000   2,000,000   3,000,000

e. _____ f. _____ g. _____ h. _____

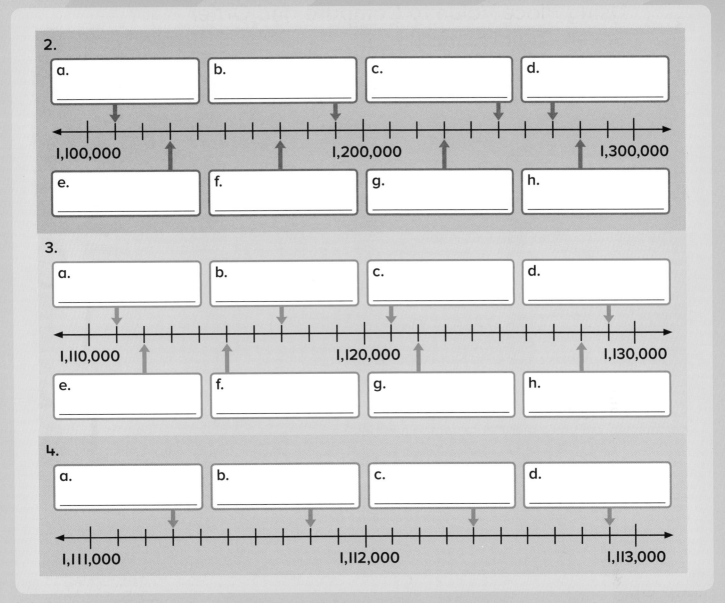

2.

a. _____ b. _____ c. _____ d. _____

1,100,000   1,200,000   1,300,000

e. _____ f. _____ g. _____ h. _____

3.

a. _____ b. _____ c. _____ d. _____

1,110,000   1,120,000   1,130,000

e. _____ f. _____ g. _____ h. _____

4.

a. _____ b. _____ c. _____ d. _____

1,111,000   1,112,000   1,113,000

Step Ahead

a. Add **twenty thousand** to this number then write the new number in words.

| 8 | millions | 0 | 5 | 6 | thousands | 0 | 0 | 9 |

_____

_____

b. Add **four hundred thousand** to this number then write the new number on the expander.

| 2 | millions | 8 | 9 | 0 | thousands | 3 | 0 | 0 |

| | millions | | | | thousands | | | |

Using Place Value to Compare and Order Seven-Digit Numbers

Look at these digit cards. Imagine you use each digit once to form a number.

Is this number possible?
How do you know?

7,013,542

5 4 7 0 1 2 1

What number(s) could you form to match these descriptions?

- The greatest number that ends in zero

- The least number that ends in zero

- Numbers between 1,000,000 and 1,100,000

- Numbers between 4,500,000 and 4,700,000

- The number that is as close to 5,000,000 as possible

- The least and greatest numbers

What strategy did you use to figure out the numbers?

Did your strategy work for every example?

Step Up   1. Look at these digit cards.

8 1 4 9 5 6 3

Use each digit once to make these.

greatest	least

a. the **greatest** and **least** numbers

b. the greatest **even** number

c. the least **even** number

d. any three numbers that are between 4,500,000 and 5,000,000

2. Roll a number cube seven times. Write the numbers you roll on these cards.

☐ ☐ ☐ ☐ ☐ ☐ ☐

Use each digit once to make these.

	greatest	least

a. the **greatest** and **least** numbers

b. the greatest **odd** number

c. the greatest **even** number

d. a number that is as close to 3,000,000 as possible _____

e. a number that is as close to 1,000,000 as possible _____

f. the three **least** numbers

_____ _____ _____

g. the three **greatest** numbers

_____ _____ _____

Step Ahead ▶ These are the top seven scores from a popular online game.

a. Write the top three scores in order from **greatest** to **least**.

1st _____

2nd _____

3rd _____

b. Write the scores for the players that came 7th, 6th, and 5th.

7th _____

6th _____

5th _____

⭐ APP SCORES ⭐

Mary	2,685,125
Andre	2,487,102
Jack	2,690,300
Rita	2,599,305
Emma	2,358,521
Franco	2,609,301
Cole	2,490,999

c. Whose score was closest to 2,500,000? _____

Reading and Writing Eight- and Nine-Digit Numbers

Where have you seen eight- or nine-digit numbers recorded?

What place values are said when you say a nine-digit number?

Complete the number name below to show how you read the number on this expander.

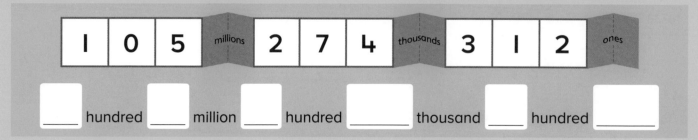

Read this number.

two hundred forty-six million seven hundred five thousand ninety

Write it on this expander.

How would you write ten million using exponential notation?

How would you write one hundred million using exponential notation?

Step Up I. Read the number name. Then write the matching number on the expander.

a. seventy-three million five hundred thirty thousand six hundred three

			millions				thousands				ones

b. four hundred eighty million five thousand three hundred fifty-eight

			millions				thousands				ones

c. seven hundred three million three thousand forty

			millions				thousands				ones

2. Write the matching number in words.

a.

| | 3 | 5 | millions | 5 | 9 | 2 | thousands | 8 | 0 | 5 | ones |

_____

_____

_____

b.

| 3 | 0 | 9 | millions | 0 | 4 | 7 | thousands | 5 | 0 | 0 | ones |

_____

_____

_____

3. Write the matching number or number words.

a.

70,293,430

_____

_____

_____

b. one hundred eight million four thousand
two hundred seventy-five

_____

c.

418,720,912

_____

_____

_____

Step Ahead Read this number name. Then write the number that is **10 million less**.

fourteen million three thousand twenty-three

_____

Draw marks to divide this number line into eight equal parts.

0   2,000,000

What number does each mark represent? How do you know?

What fraction of one million does the third mark represent? How do you know?

Label the whole number below the line and the fraction above the line for each mark.

What quarter million is closest to
1,483,000? How did you figure it out?

Step Up

1. Draw an arrow to show the position of each number on the number line.
   Be as accurate as possible.

a.

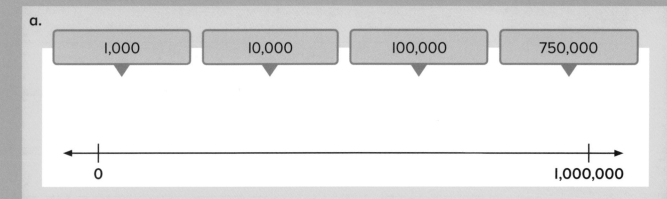

| 1,000 | 10,000 | 100,000 | 750,000 |

0   1,000,000

b.

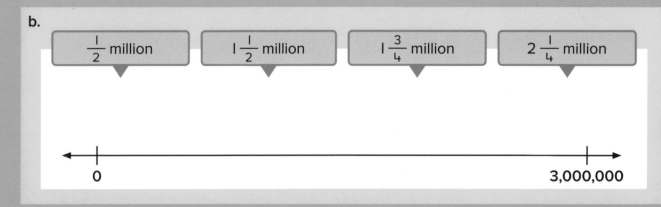

| $\frac{1}{2}$ million | $1\frac{1}{2}$ million | $1\frac{3}{4}$ million | $2\frac{1}{4}$ million |

0   3,000,000

2. Write each expression as a whole number.

a. $\frac{1}{4}$ million _____

b. $4\frac{1}{2}$ million _____

c. $2\frac{3}{4}$ million _____

d. $3\frac{1}{4}$ million _____

3. Look at this list of populations. Which state has a population closest to each of these?

POPULATION	
Alaska	731,449
Colorado	5,187,582
Connecticut	3,590,347
Indiana	6,537,334
Nevada	2,758,931
New Jersey	8,864,590
New Mexico	2,085,538
North Carolina	9,752,073
Tennessee	6,456,243
Wisconsin	5,726,398

a. $5\frac{3}{4}$ million _____

b. 2 million _____

c. $8\frac{3}{4}$ million _____

d. $6\frac{1}{2}$ million _____

e. $2\frac{3}{4}$ million _____

f. $5\frac{1}{4}$ million _____

4. Look at this list of state populations.
Write the state that has a population closest to each of these.

POPULATION	
Idaho	1,595,728
Louisiana	4,601,893
Mississippi	2,984,926
South Carolina	4,723,723
Utah	2,855,287
West Virginia	1,855,413

a. 3.0 million _____

b. 1.75 million _____

c. 4.5 million _____

d. 2.75 million _____

Step Ahead

Look at the list from Question 3. Round the populations of these states to the nearest $\frac{1}{4}$ million. Write the fraction.

a. Connecticut [ ] million

b. Alaska [ ] million

How could you calculate the area of each rectangle?

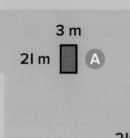

What number sentences could you write to show what you did?

Complete this place-value chart.

	Th	H	T	Ones
21 × 3 =				
210 × 3 =				
210 × 30 =				

What do you notice about the products?

How can you use the product for the first sentence to figure out the product for the second sentence?

Except for the zero, the same digits appear in the products but in different places.

Step Up ▶ 1. Calculate the area. Use a pattern to help you.

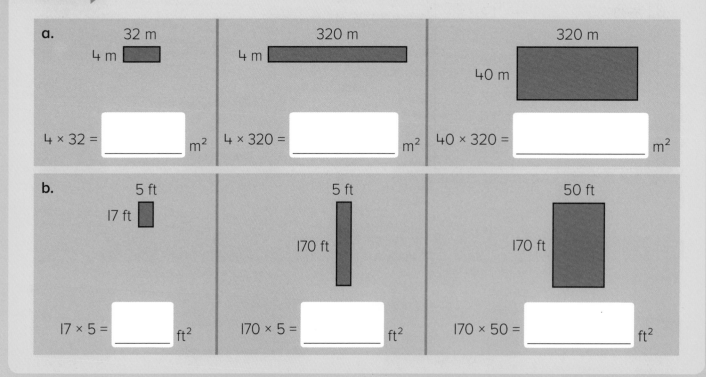

a.

32 m
4 m

4 × 32 = _____ m²

320 m
4 m

4 × 320 = _____ m²

320 m
40 m

40 × 320 = _____ m²

b.

5 ft
17 ft

17 × 5 = _____ ft²

5 ft
170 ft

170 × 5 = _____ ft²

50 ft
170 ft

170 × 50 = _____ ft²

2. Use a pattern to help you write the products.

a.

	Th	H	T	Ones
16 × 3 =				
16 × 30 =				
160 × 30 =				

b.

	Th	H	T	Ones
17 × 4 =				
17 × 40 =				
170 × 40 =				

c.

	Th	H	T	Ones
15 × 5 =				
15 × 50 =				
150 × 50 =				

d.

	Th	H	T	Ones
13 × 6 =				
13 × 60 =				
130 × 60 =				

e.

	Th	H	T	Ones
16 × 6 =				
16 × 60 =				
160 × 60 =				

f.

	Th	H	T	Ones
14 × 7 =				
14 × 70 =				
140 × 70 =				

g.

	Th	H	T	Ones
12 × 7 =				
12 × 70 =				
120 × 70 =				

h.

	Th	H	T	Ones
23 × 4 =				
23 × 40 =				
230 × 40 =				

Step Ahead

Write the numbers that are **10 times more** and **100 times more**. Then complete each number sentence.

a.

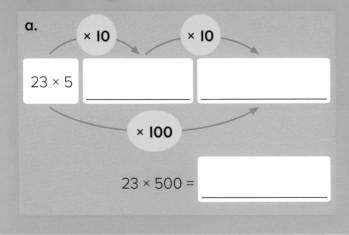

23 × 500 = _____

b.

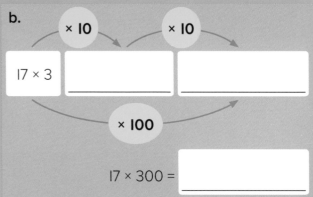

17 × 300 = _____

Reviewing the Double-and-Halve Strategy for Multiplication

I want to lay turf in an area that measures 12 yd by 15 yd. How many square yards of turf will I need?

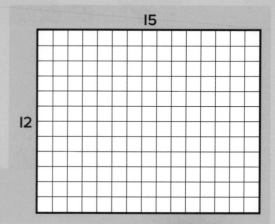

15

12

Look at this array. How could you figure out the number of square yards without counting all the squares?

I would cut the array into two pieces. Then I would multiply 10 x 15 and 2 x 15.

You could also double and halve.
Imagine the array above is cut in half and rearranged like this.

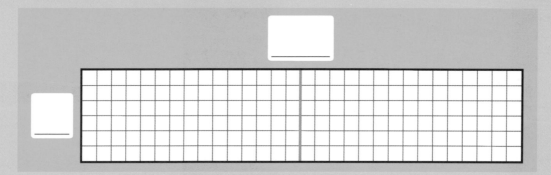

Has the total number of squares changed? Label the new dimensions.

Are these numbers easier to multiply in your head?

How will 6 × 30 change if you doubled and halved it again?

Step Up

1. Double one number and halve the other to make a problem that is easier to solve. Then write the product.

a. **15 × 14**

_____ × _____

15 × 14 = _____

b. **16 × 15**

_____ × _____

16 × 15 = _____

c. **35 × 8**

_____ × _____

35 × 8 = _____

2. Double and halve twice to solve each of these.

a. 15×28

$$\underline{\hspace{2cm}} \times \underline{\hspace{2cm}}$$

$$\underline{\hspace{2cm}} \times \underline{\hspace{2cm}}$$

$15 \times 28 = \underline{\hspace{2cm}}$

b. 13×16

$$\underline{\hspace{2cm}} \times \underline{\hspace{2cm}}$$

$$\underline{\hspace{2cm}} \times \underline{\hspace{2cm}}$$

$13 \times 16 = \underline{\hspace{2cm}}$

c. 28×25

$$\underline{\hspace{2cm}} \times \underline{\hspace{2cm}}$$

$$\underline{\hspace{2cm}} \times \underline{\hspace{2cm}}$$

$28 \times 25 = \underline{\hspace{2cm}}$

3. Calculate the products. Show the steps you use.

a. $25 \times 24 = \underline{\hspace{2cm}}$

b. $45 \times 16 = \underline{\hspace{2cm}}$

c. $18 \times 4 = \underline{\hspace{2cm}}$

d. $8 \times 23 = \underline{\hspace{2cm}}$

e. $14 \times 12 = \underline{\hspace{2cm}}$

f. $12 \times 55 = \underline{\hspace{2cm}}$

Step Ahead   Write different pairs of **two-digit** numbers to match each product.

a.

$\underline{\hspace{1.5cm}} \times \underline{\hspace{1.5cm}} = 800$

$\underline{\hspace{1.5cm}} \times \underline{\hspace{1.5cm}} = 800$

$\underline{\hspace{1.5cm}} \times \underline{\hspace{1.5cm}} = 800$

b.

$\underline{\hspace{1.5cm}} \times \underline{\hspace{1.5cm}} = 720$

$\underline{\hspace{1.5cm}} \times \underline{\hspace{1.5cm}} = 720$

$\underline{\hspace{1.5cm}} \times \underline{\hspace{1.5cm}} = 720$

Factoring to Multiply Two-Digit Numbers

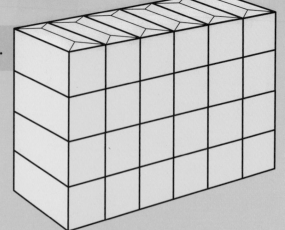

There are 15 small boxes inside each of these large boxes.

Write a multiplication sentence you could use to figure out the total number of small boxes in all the large boxes.

_____

How would you calculate the total in your head?

> I used factors to make the multiplication easier.

How would you multiply 3 × 5 × 6 × 4?
Which factors would you multiply first? Why?

What is the total number of small boxes?

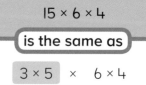

15 × 6 × 4

(is the same as)

3 × 5 × 6 × 4

Claire counted 36 pine trees in one square of this field.

How could Claire estimate the total number of trees in the whole field if there are about the same number in each square?

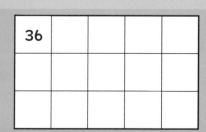

36			

Step Up

1. Break **one** number into two factors to make it easier to multiply. Then complete the equation.

a.
35 × 8   is the same as   ☐ × ☐ × ☐ = ☐

b.
6 × 35   is the same as   ☐ × ☐ × ☐ = ☐

c.
25 × 28   is the same as   ☐ × ☐ × ☐ = ☐

d.
45 × 4   is the same as   ☐ × ☐ × ☐ = ☐

e.
12 × 15   is the same as   ☐ × ☐ × ☐ = ☐

2. Break **both** numbers into two factors. Then complete the equation.

a.
12 × 24   is the same as   ☐ × ☐ × ☐ × ☐ = ☐

b.
18 × 55   is the same as   ☐ × ☐ × ☐ × ☐ = ☐

c.
40 × 18   is the same as   ☐ × ☐ × ☐ × ☐ = ☐

d.
36 × 15   is the same as   ☐ × ☐ × ☐ × ☐ = ☐

e.
45 × 16   is the same as   ☐ × ☐ × ☐ × ☐ = ☐

3. Break **one** or **both** numbers into two factors to make it easier to multiply.
Then write the matching equation.

a.
25 × 16   is the same as

b.
35 × 18   is the same as

c.
15 × 16   is the same as

d.
14 × 25   is the same as

e.
35 × 16   is the same as

f.
14 × 45   is the same as

Step Ahead

For each of these, write the product. Then write the different pairs of **two-digit** numbers that may have been factored to create these equations.

a.
5 × 2 × 6 × 9 = ☐

b.
3 × 5 × 8 × 7 = ☐

Using Partial Products to Multiply (Distributive Property)

How could you figure out the total number of squares in this array?

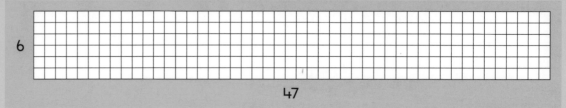

6

47

You could break 47 into tens and ones like this.

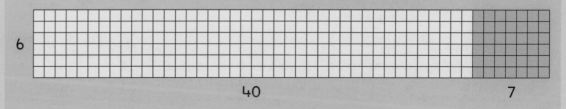

6

40

7

What number sentence could you write to describe each part of the array?

What number sentence could you write to describe the total number of squares?

Is there another way you could figure it out?

Step Up

1. Calculate the partial products to figure out each of these.
Then write the total.

a.	26 × 3

$20 \times 3 = \underline{\hspace{1cm}}$

$6 \times 3 = \underline{\hspace{1cm}}$

$26 \times 3 = \boxed{}$

b.	34 × 4

$30 \times 4 = \underline{\hspace{1cm}}$

$4 \times 4 = \underline{\hspace{1cm}}$

$\underline{\hspace{0.5cm}} \times \boxed{} = \boxed{}$

c.	58 × 5

$\underline{\hspace{1cm}} \times 5 = \underline{\hspace{1cm}}$

$\underline{\hspace{1cm}} \times 5 = \underline{\hspace{1cm}}$

$\underline{\hspace{0.5cm}} \times \boxed{} = \boxed{}$

d.	64 × 7

$\underline{\hspace{1cm}} \times \underline{\hspace{1cm}} = \underline{\hspace{1cm}}$

$\underline{\hspace{1cm}} \times \underline{\hspace{1cm}} = \underline{\hspace{1cm}}$

$\boxed{} \times \boxed{} = \boxed{}$

e.	73 × 6

$\underline{\hspace{1cm}} \times \underline{\hspace{1cm}} = \underline{\hspace{1cm}}$

$\underline{\hspace{1cm}} \times \underline{\hspace{1cm}} = \underline{\hspace{1cm}}$

$\boxed{} \times \boxed{} = \boxed{}$

f.	87 × 4

$\underline{\hspace{1cm}} \times \underline{\hspace{1cm}} = \underline{\hspace{1cm}}$

$\underline{\hspace{1cm}} \times \underline{\hspace{1cm}} = \underline{\hspace{1cm}}$

$\boxed{} \times \boxed{} = \boxed{}$

2. Figure out each product. Show the steps you use.

a.

$78 \times 4 =$ _____

b.

$67 \times 8 =$ _____

c.

$43 \times 6 =$ _____

d.

$36 \times 7 =$ _____

e.

$54 \times 3 =$ _____

f.

$87 \times 6 =$ _____

g.

$38 \times 6 =$ _____

h.

$3 \times 86 =$ _____

i.

$7 \times 93 =$ _____

Step Ahead A student continues to make the same error in a math test. Write the correct product above each of these. Then explain the error that is being made.

a. $39 \times 4 = 48$

$3 \times 4 = 12$

$9 \times 4 = 36$

b. $56 \times 7 = 77$

$5 \times 7 = 35$

$6 \times 7 = 42$

c. $48 \times 9 = 108$

$4 \times 9 = 36$

$8 \times 9 = 72$

d. $37 \times 8 = 80$

$3 \times 8 = 24$

$7 \times 8 = 56$

_____

_____

_____

Think about some of the different situations in which you use multiplication.

Multiplication is often used to figure out the cost of purchases.

Imagine you have to buy carpet for this floor area. Look at how these students figure out the area that has to be covered.

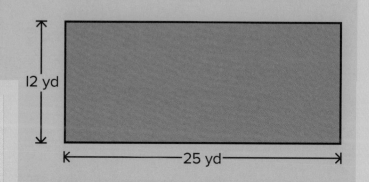

12 yd

25 yd

Emily used partial products.

10 × 25 + 2 × 25

Cody used a doubling-and-halving strategy.

12 × 25 is the same as 6 × 50

Daniel used factors.

12 × 25 is the same as 3 × 4 × 25

Is there another way you could figure it out? Which way do you like best? Why?

Use a strategy you like to calculate the area of a rectangle measuring 15 cm × 24 cm.

Step Up ▶ Read these strategies for mentally calculating 36 × 50.

I multiplied 36 by 10. Then I multiplied my answer by 5 because 50 is 5 x 10.

I multiplied 36 by 100. Then I halved my answer because 50 is one-half of 100.

1. Try to use more than one method from page 30 to solve these.

a. 16 × 50 = [ ]

b. 24 × 50 = [ ]

c. 25 × 50 = [ ]

d. 27 × 50 = [ ]

e. 15 × 50 = [ ]

f. 14 × 50 = [ ]

2. Use a method you like to mentally calculate these.

a. 72 × 50 = [ ]

b. 34 × 50 = [ ]

c. 64 × 50 = [ ]

d. 42 × 50 = [ ]

e. 28 × 50 = [ ]

f. 31 × 50 = [ ]

3. Write how you could mentally figure out 32 × 25.

[ ]

4. Use your method from Question 3 to mentally calculate these.

a. 24 × 25 = [ ]

b. 16 × 25 = [ ]

c. 28 × 25 = [ ]

d. 44 × 25 = [ ]

e. 12 × 25 = [ ]

f. 36 × 25 = [ ]

5. Complete number sentences you can solve using your method from Question 3.

a. [ ] × 50 = [ ]

b. 50 × [ ] = [ ]

Step Ahead Write the missing numbers in each machine.

a.

IN		OUT
12		
22	× 150	
18		

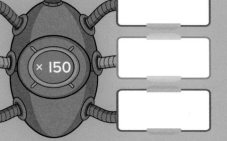

b.

IN		OUT
12		
22	× 500	
18		

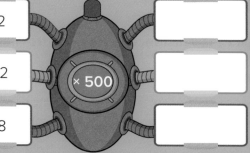

Reviewing Common Fractions and Mixed Numbers (Number Line Model)

On each number line, the distance from 0 to 1 represents one mile.

These students each marked the distance they live from school on the number lines below.

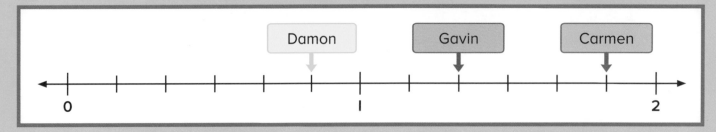

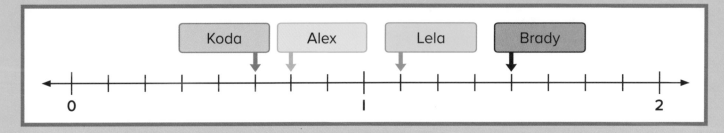

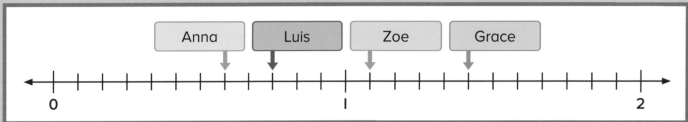

What types of numbers could be used to record these distances?

The distances must be shown as common fractions or mixed numbers.

What distance do you think Damon recorded? How do you know?

Which students marked distances that were a little more than one mile? How do you know? What distance do you think each of these students marked?

Look at the distance Brady lives from the school.

Why could this distance be written more than one way?

Choose two other students who marked a distance that could be written in more than one way. What are the different ways you could write the distances for these students?

1. Look at the distances marked on page 32. Write the distance you think each of these students marked.

Carmen	Koda	Anna	Grace
mi	mi	mi	mi

2. Look at the number lines below.

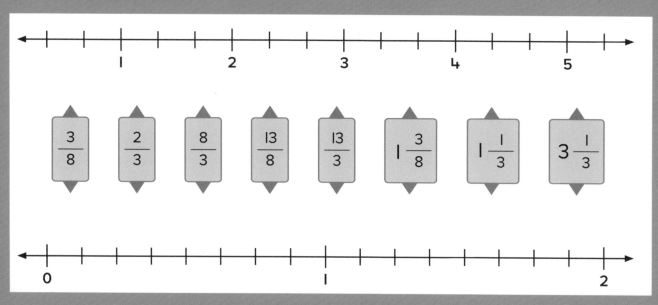

a. For each number line, write a fraction name to describe the size of the unit fractions in one whole.

The top number line	The bottom number line

b. Look at the fractions and mixed numbers shown between the number lines above. Draw an arrow from each fraction and mixed number to show its position on one number line.

Convert these times.
You can use the clock to help you.

$1\frac{1}{4}$ hours = _____ min

$2\frac{1}{2}$ hours = _____ min

_____ hours = 135 min

$1\frac{1}{2}$ hours = _____ min

_____ hours = 210 min

_____ hour = 45 min

Sheree's dad has a rectangular garden bed split into equal parts. The shaded part of this diagram shows how much of the garden has been planted.

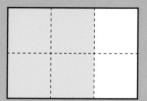

What fraction of the garden has been planted?

Sheree's dad decided to split the garden bed into a different number of equal parts. The same amount of the garden has been planted.

Look at this diagram. How did he split the garden bed?

Write the fraction of the garden that is planted.

What do you notice about the two fractions you wrote?

I can see that the value of the denominator in the second fraction is double the value of the denominator in the first fraction. The value of the numerator is also double.

> Fractions are **equivalent** if they cover the same area of each shape.

Complete this diagram to show how the fractions are related.

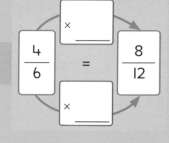

Imagine Sheree's dad planted the whole garden.
Color more parts of the two diagrams above to show the change.

What fraction would you write to match the amount that is planted in the first diagram? What whole number would you write?

What fraction would you write to match the amount that is planted in the second diagram? What whole number would you write?

What do you notice?

Think about how you would compare $\frac{3}{8}$ and $\frac{4}{16}$.

What do you need to do first?
How could you use this diagram to help you?

Which amount is greater?

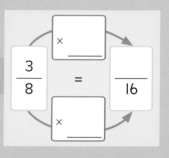

1. Complete these to show equivalent fractions.

a.

b.

c.

d.
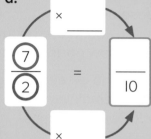

2. For each of these, write the fraction and then write four fractions that are equivalent.

a. two-thirds
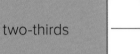

b. six-fourths
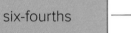

c. thirty-twelfths

3. Change one fraction in each pair so that they have the same denominator. Then rewrite the fractions.

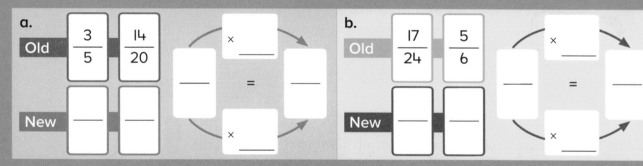

Use each number only once to write three pairs of equivalent fractions.

| 1 | 2 | 3 | 4 | 5 | 6 | 7 | 8 | 12 | 18 | 20 | 21 |

  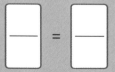

Reviewing Equivalent Common Fractions (Related and Unrelated Denominators)

Look at this multiplication chart.

Choose one row of numbers.
What do you notice about the numbers in the yellow parts of that row?

Imagine the green parts were cut off the grid and the remaining parts were cut horizontally into 10 separate strips.

These two strips have been placed one above the other. What do you notice?

×	1	2	3	4	5	6	7	8	9	10
1	1	2	3	4	5	6	7	8	9	10
2	2	4	6	8	10	12	14	16	18	20
3	3	6	9	12	15	18	21	24	27	30
4	4	8	12	16	20	24	28	32	36	40
5	5	10	15	20	25	30	35	40	45	50
6	6	12	18	24	30	36	42	48	54	60
7	7	14	21	28	35	42	49	56	63	70
8	8	16	24	32	40	48	56	64	72	80
9	9	18	27	36	45	54	63	72	81	90
10	10	20	30	40	50	60	70	80	90	100

3	6	9	12	15	18	21	24	27	30
8	16	24	32	40	48	56	64	72	80

The first two numbers look like the fraction $\frac{3}{8}$ and the second two look like the fraction $\frac{6}{16}$.

What other fractions can you see in the two strips? Write two of them.

What do you notice about all four fractions?

All the fractions are related because the denominators are all multiples of 8. I can also see that if I double the numerator and the denominator of $\frac{6}{16}$ it makes $\frac{12}{32}$.

Complete this diagram to show how $\frac{3}{8}$ is equivalent to $\frac{15}{40}$.

What do you notice?

How could you figure out which is greater? $\frac{4}{5}$ or $\frac{3}{4}$

What is a denominator they have in common?

How could you use the rows of the multiplication chart to help you?

Try multiplying both denominators together. What do you notice?

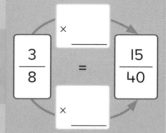

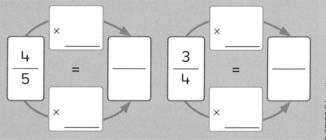

1. For each pair of fractions, write equivalent fractions that have denominators the same. Write the missing factors to show your thinking.

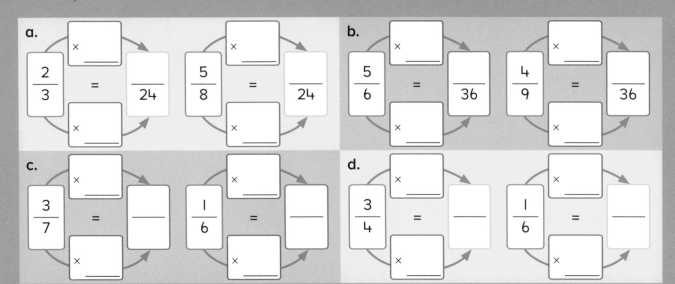

a.

$\frac{2}{3}$ × ___ = $\frac{}{24}$ × ___ $\frac{5}{8}$ × ___ = $\frac{}{24}$ × ___

b.

$\frac{5}{6}$ × ___ = $\frac{}{36}$ × ___ $\frac{4}{9}$ × ___ = $\frac{}{36}$ × ___

c.

$\frac{3}{7}$ × ___ = $\frac{}{}$ × ___ $\frac{1}{6}$ × ___ = $\frac{}{}$ × ___

d.

$\frac{3}{4}$ × ___ = $\frac{}{}$ × ___ $\frac{1}{6}$ × ___ = $\frac{}{}$ × ___

2. Rewrite both fractions so the denominators are the same.

a. $\frac{1}{4} = \frac{}{}$ $\frac{1}{3} = \frac{}{}$

b. $\frac{2}{6} = \frac{}{}$ $\frac{1}{2} = \frac{}{}$

c. $\frac{4}{3} = \frac{}{}$ $\frac{2}{5} = \frac{}{}$

d. $\frac{2}{5} = \frac{}{}$ $\frac{7}{12} = \frac{}{}$

e. $\frac{6}{5} = \frac{}{}$ $\frac{5}{6} = \frac{}{}$

f. $\frac{9}{4} = \frac{}{}$ $\frac{9}{6} = \frac{}{}$

3. Look at the fractions in the red boxes in Questions 1 and 2 above. Loop the greater fraction in each pair.

Unit fractions have a 1 as the numerator.

a. Shade this strip to show a fraction that is equivalent to a unit fraction.

b. Shade these strips to show fractions that are equivalent to two **other** unit fractions.

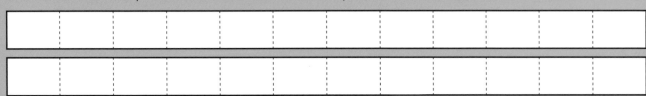

A recipe uses $\frac{3}{4}$ cup of milk to make one batch of 8 pancakes.

Manuel wants to make **6** batches of pancakes so he will need $6 \times \frac{3}{4}$ or $\frac{18}{4}$ cups of milk.

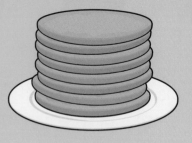

How many **whole cups** of milk will he need?

How could you figure it out?

> I know that 4 one-fourths makes one whole, and 8 one-fourths makes two wholes. I need to find out how many wholes I can make with 18 one-fourths.

> I think there might be leftovers involved.

> A **proper fraction** has a numerator that is less than or equal to its denominator. An **improper fraction** has a numerator that is greater than its denominator.

How do you write $\frac{18}{4}$ as a mixed number?

Step Up ▶

I. Rewrite each improper fraction as a mixed number. Show your thinking.

a.

$\frac{9}{4}$ is the same as ▶ ☐

b.

$\frac{5}{2}$ is the same as ▶ ☐

c.

$\frac{8}{3}$ is the same as ▶ ☐

d.

$\frac{15}{8}$ is the same as ▶ ☐

2. Rewrite each improper fraction as a mixed number. Show your thinking.

a.

$\frac{14}{6}$ is the same as ▢

b.

$\frac{32}{10}$ is the same as ▢

c.

$\frac{34}{5}$ is the same as ▢

d.

$\frac{27}{12}$ is the same as ▢

3. Read each story and write the total as a **mixed number**. Show your thinking.

a. One box weighs $\frac{3}{4}$ pound. Nine of those boxes together weigh $\frac{27}{4}$ pounds.

_____ lb

b. One hair ribbon is $\frac{5}{6}$ of a yard long. To make 7 ribbons, $\frac{35}{6}$ yd of ribbon is needed.

_____ yd

Step Ahead   Look at the fractions and mixed numbers. Loop the greater amount in each pair.

a. $1\frac{5}{6}$ or $\frac{10}{6}$

b. $2\frac{3}{4}$ or $\frac{23}{8}$

c. $\frac{5}{3}$ or $1\frac{4}{12}$

Working Space

Ashley changed $2\frac{4}{5}$ to an improper fraction. She drew this picture to show her thinking.

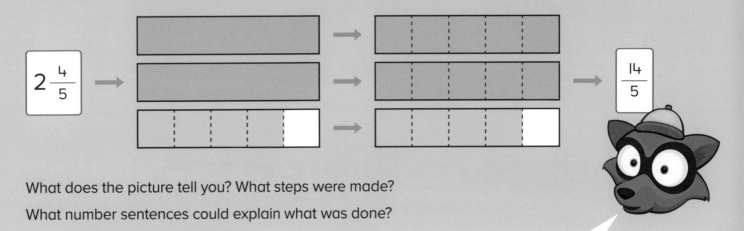

What does the picture tell you? What steps were made?

What number sentences could explain what was done?

> The denominator tells me that we are working with fifths.
> I need to think about how many one-fifths are equal to 2 wholes.

Sumi showed her thinking this way.

$2\frac{4}{5}$ → $2+\frac{4}{5}$ → $1+1\frac{4}{5}$ → $\frac{5}{5}+\frac{5}{5}+\frac{4}{5}$ → $\frac{10}{5}+\frac{4}{5}$ → $\frac{14}{5}$

Liam showed his thinking like this.

$2\frac{4}{5}$ → $2+\frac{4}{5}$ → $\frac{2\times5}{5}+\frac{4}{5}$ → $\frac{10}{5}+\frac{4}{5}$ → $\frac{14}{5}$

How do Sumi's and Liam's methods relate to the picture Ashley drew?

How do they relate to each other?

How could you use these methods to change $5\frac{2}{6}$ to an improper fraction?

Step Up

1. Adjust this picture to show how $2\frac{3}{4}$ is the same as $\frac{11}{4}$.

$2\frac{3}{4}$ → → $\frac{11}{4}$

2. Rewrite each mixed number as an improper fraction. Show your thinking.

a.

$4 \frac{2}{3}$ is the same as ➡ $\frac{}{}$

b.

$5 \frac{2}{6}$ is the same as ➡ $\frac{}{}$

c.

$2 \frac{3}{8}$ is the same as ➡ $\frac{}{}$

d.

$4 \frac{3}{5}$ is the same as ➡ $\frac{}{}$

e.

$6 \frac{3}{10}$ is the same as ➡ $\frac{}{}$

Step Ahead Jacob used these steps to rewrite $3 \frac{2}{5}$ as an improper fraction. What mistake did he make?

$$3 \frac{2}{5} \rightarrow 3 + \frac{2}{5} \rightarrow \frac{3 \times 5}{5} + \frac{3 \times 2}{5} \rightarrow \frac{15}{5} + \frac{6}{5} \rightarrow \frac{21}{5}$$

_____

_____

Look at these two fractions.

What strategy would you use to decide which is greater?

$\dfrac{2}{3}$ $\dfrac{4}{5}$

I would compare them to the benchmark 1.
They are both less than 1.

$\frac{2}{3}$ is $\frac{1}{3}$ away from 1 but $\frac{4}{5}$ is only $\frac{1}{5}$ away from 1.

I would find a common denominator.

Complete this diagram to find equivalent fractions with a common denominator.

Write **<** or **>** in the circle to make a true statement.

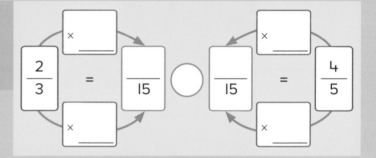

$\dfrac{2}{3}$ = $\dfrac{}{15}$ ◯ $\dfrac{}{15}$ = $\dfrac{4}{5}$

Is there another way you could compare $\frac{2}{3}$ and $\frac{4}{5}$?

I could find a common numerator.

Step Up ▶

I. Compare the fractions in each pair to a benchmark such as $\frac{1}{2}$ or 1.
Then write **<** or **>** to make a true statement. Write your thinking.

a.
$\dfrac{6}{7}$ ◯ $\dfrac{8}{9}$ _____

_____

b.
$\dfrac{4}{6}$ ◯ $\dfrac{3}{8}$ _____

_____

2. Write **<** or **>** to make each statement true. Write or show your thinking.

a.

$\dfrac{1}{5}$ ◯ $\dfrac{1}{4}$

b.

$\dfrac{3}{4}$ ◯ $\dfrac{5}{8}$

c.

$\dfrac{5}{6}$ ◯ $\dfrac{9}{10}$

d.

$\dfrac{3}{8}$ ◯ $\dfrac{6}{10}$

e.

$\dfrac{6}{5}$ ◯ $\dfrac{3}{2}$

f.

$\dfrac{6}{4}$ ◯ $\dfrac{9}{8}$

Step Ahead Write these fractions in order from **least** to **greatest**.

$\dfrac{5}{2}$ $\dfrac{7}{3}$ $\dfrac{13}{5}$ $\underline{}$ $\underline{}$ $\underline{}$

Write or show your thinking.

This large square represents one whole.
Color parts to match the number on the expander below.

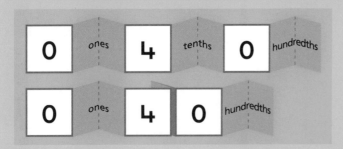

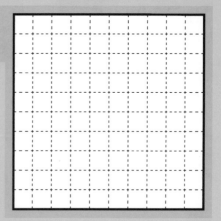

What common fractions could you write to match 0.4? How do you know?

Color more parts to show a total of 0.75 shaded.
What common fraction could you write to match?

On this number line, the distance between each whole number is one whole.

Mark the position of 0.4 and 0.75 on the number line.

Where would you mark 1.35 on the number line?

What mixed number would you write to match 1.35?

What are some other decimal fractions that you could show?

Step Up ▶ I. Each large square is one whole. Shade parts to show the decimal fraction. Then write the matching common fraction.

a.

0.55 is the same as $\frac{55}{100}$

b.

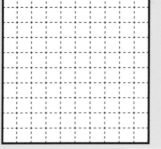
0.8 is the same as ───

c.

 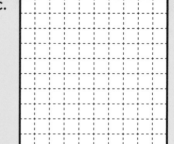
0.15 is the same as ───

2. Complete these in the same way as Question I.

a.

0.01 is the same as ____

b.

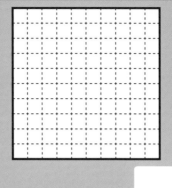

0.3 is the same as ____

c.

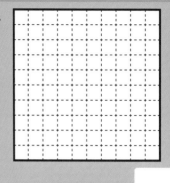

0.45 is the same as ____

3. Draw a line to show the location of each decimal fraction. Be as accurate as possible.

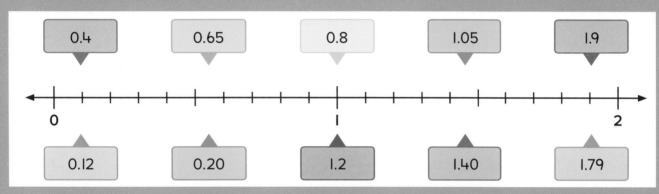

4. Write the decimal fraction to match each common fraction.

a. $\frac{85}{100}$ is the same as 0. _____

b. $\frac{6}{10}$ is the same as 0. _____

c. $\frac{90}{100}$ is the same as 0. _____

Step Ahead Color parts to show a fraction that matches each description.

a. greater than 0.6 but less than $\frac{4}{5}$

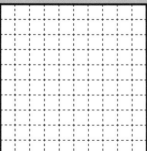

b. less than $\frac{3}{4}$ but greater than 0.5

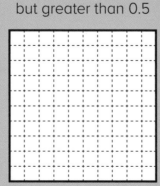

c. more than 0.8 but less than I

What do you call one of the ten equal parts that form one whole number?

Complete the **first row** of this table to show what you write.

Fraction word	Ones	tenths	hundredths	thousandths	Decimal fraction	Common fraction
	0	1	0	0	0.1	

What do you call one of the ten equal parts that form one-tenth?

Complete the **second row** of the table to show what you write.

The large square below is one whole. How has it been divided?

What do you call one of the ten equal parts that form one-hundredth?

Complete the **third row** of the table to show what you write.

Color parts of the large square to match the decimal fraction on the expander.

0 ones 4 tenths 9 hundredths 5 thousandths

Step Up

Each large square is one whole. Shade parts of the whole to match the decimal fraction on the expander.

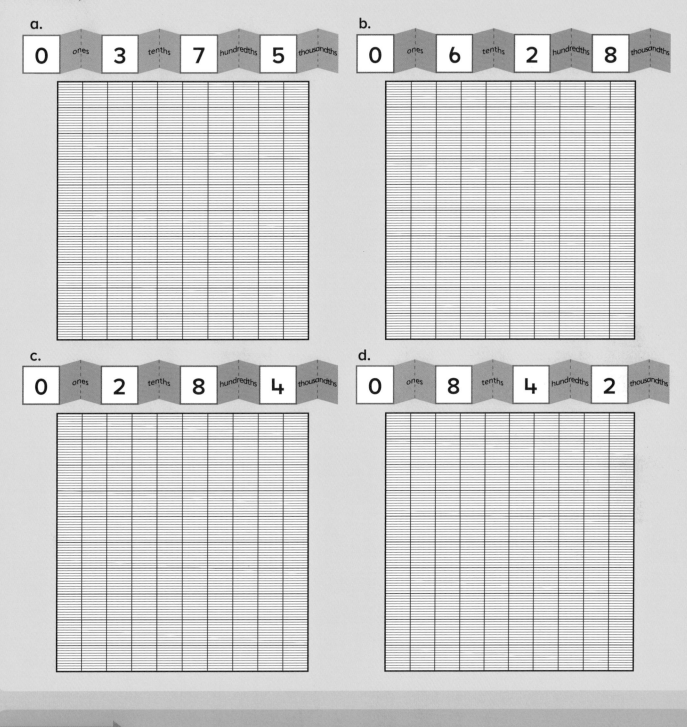

a.

| 0 | ones | 3 | tenths | 7 | hundredths | 5 | thousandths |

b.

| 0 | ones | 6 | tenths | 2 | hundredths | 8 | thousandths |

c.

| 0 | ones | 2 | tenths | 8 | hundredths | 4 | thousandths |

d.

| 0 | ones | 8 | tenths | 4 | hundredths | 2 | thousandths |

Step Ahead

This strip is one whole.

Explain how you could divide the strip into hundredths and then thousandths.

_____

_____

Reading and Writing Thousandths (without Zeros and Teens)

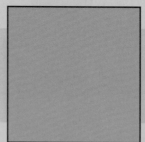
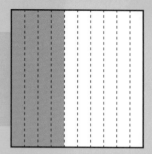

Each large square is one whole.

What fraction has been shaded?
How do you know?

Write the mixed number that matches the shaded amount. Then write the equivalent decimal fraction on the expander.

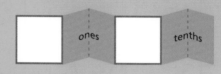

Imagine you drew more lines to divide the tenths into hundredths.

How many hundredths would be shaded? How could you read this number?

Write the mixed number that matches the amount that would be shaded. Then write the equivalent decimal fraction on the expander.

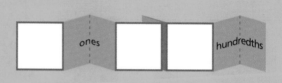

Imagine you drew more lines to divide the hundredths into thousandths.

How many thousandths would be shaded? How could you read this number?

Write a mixed number to show the fraction that would be shaded. Then write the equivalent decimal fraction on the expander.

Look at this place-value chart.

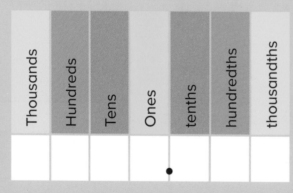

What do you notice about the places on either side of the ones place?

Write **one and four hundred thousandths** on the chart.

1. Write the matching number with and then without the expander.

a. four and six hundred thousandths

b. four and six hundred thirty thousandths

2. Complete the missing parts.

a.

$9\dfrac{352}{1000}$

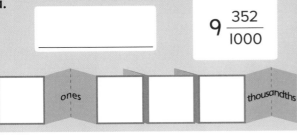

nine and three hundred

fifty-two thousandths

b.

4.562

c.

| 3 | ones | 4 | 7 | 1 | thousandths |

d.

1.375

Step Ahead Use the digits 2, 4, 5, and 9 to write four different decimal fractions that are all greater than 2 but less than 3.

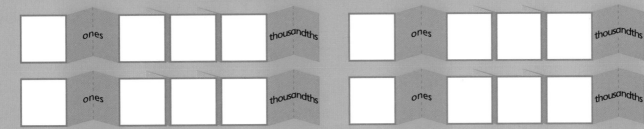

2.10 ▸ Reading and Writing Thousandths (with Zeros and Teens)

This large square is one whole.

Color parts of the square to match the decimal fraction on this expander.

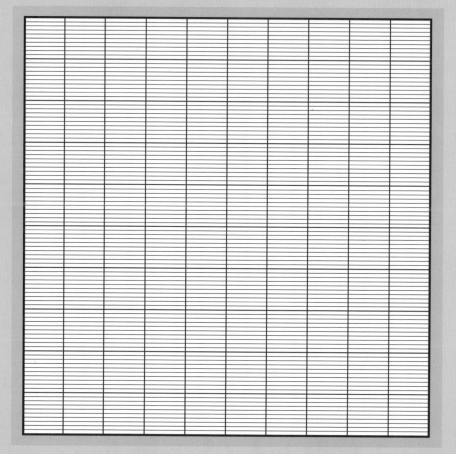

How did you know what number of parts to color? How would you read the number?

Seven hundred five thousandths.

What common fraction could you write to match 0.705?

Color more parts to show 0.730. What common fractions could you write to match 0.730?

Step Up   I. Write the matching decimal fraction with and then without the expander.

a. two and four hundred eighty thousandths

b. five and one hundred nine thousandths

2. Complete the missing parts.

a.

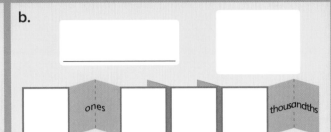

$$7\frac{208}{1000}$$

| 7 | ones | 2 | 0 | 8 | thousandths |

_____

b.

| | ones | | | | thousandths |

five and nine hundred

three thousandths

c.

3.590

| | ones | | | | thousandths |

_____

d.

1.095

| | ones | | | | thousandths |

_____

Step Ahead ▶ Write numbers on the blank expanders so that each pair of expanders shows equivalent amounts.

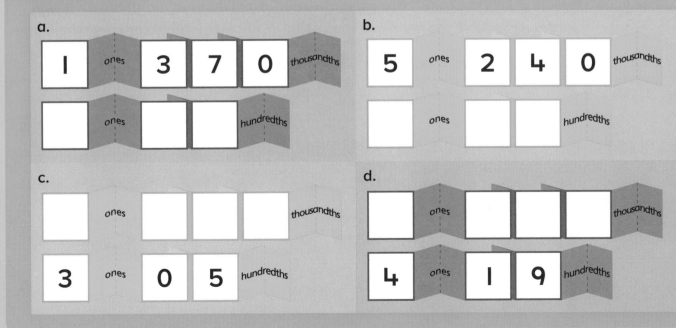

a.

| 1 | ones | 3 | 7 | 0 | thousandths |
| | ones | | | hundredths |

b.

| 5 | ones | 2 | 4 | 0 | thousandths |
| | ones | | | hundredths |

c.

| | ones | | | | thousandths |
| 3 | ones | 0 | 5 | hundredths |

d.

| | ones | | | | thousandths |
| 4 | ones | 1 | 9 | hundredths |

On each number line, the distance between each whole number is one whole.

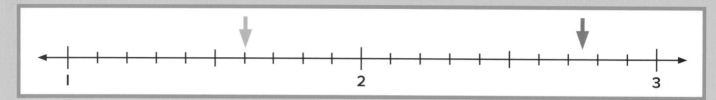

What decimal fraction describes the position marked by the orange arrow?

How could you figure out the decimal fraction that the green arrow is indicating?

> You need to split the number line into smaller parts.

This smaller part of the same number line has been split into hundredths.

What decimal fraction describes the position marked by the green arrow? How do you know?

This smaller part of the same number line has been split into thousandths.

What decimal fractions would you say between 2.750 and 2.760?

Step Up

I. Write the decimal fraction that is shown by each arrow.

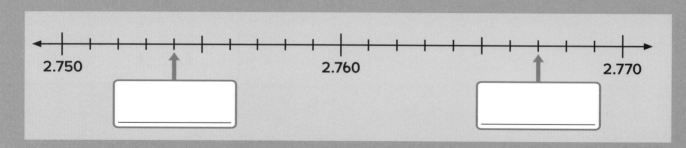

2. Write the decimal fraction that is shown by each arrow.

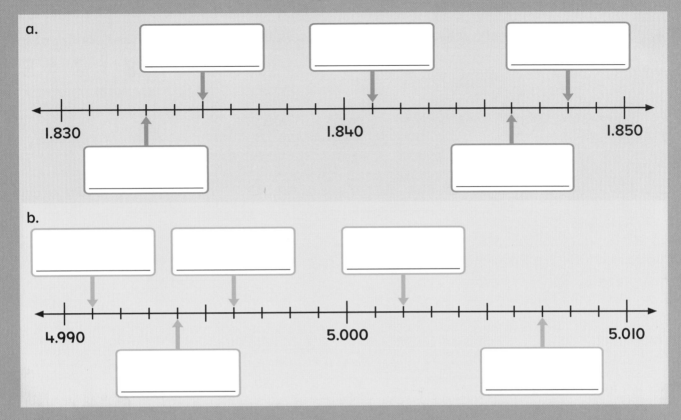

a.

1.830   1.840   1.850

b.

4.990   5.000   5.010

3. Draw an arrow to connect each decimal fraction to its approximate position on the number line. Be as accurate as possible.

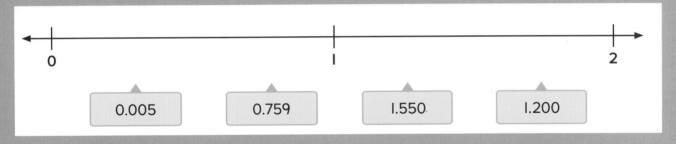

0   1   2

0.005   0.759   1.550   1.200

Step Ahead

Three friends estimated the position of 0.090 on a number line. Who do you think is most accurate? Explain your thinking.

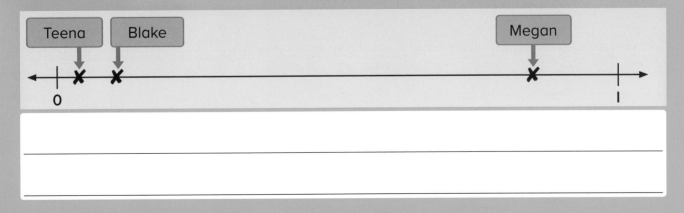

Teena   Blake   Megan

0   1

2.12 ▶ Decomposing Thousandths

How do you say the decimal fraction on this closed expander?

What mixed number could you write to match?

| 3. | 8 | 7 | 5 |

Look at this open expander. How could you break 3.875 into parts?

| 3 | ones | 8 | tenths | 7 | hundredths | 5 | thousandths |

Kayla wrote this number sentence.

$3.875 = 3 + 0.8 + 0.07 + $ ____

Victor wrote this number sentence.

$3.875 = 3 + \dfrac{8}{10} + \dfrac{7}{100} + $ ____

Write the missing addend in each sentence.

How does each person break 3.875 into parts?

Can you think of another way to break 3.875 into parts?

38 tenths + 75 thousandths.

Step Up

1. Write an addition expression that uses decimal fractions to break each number into parts.

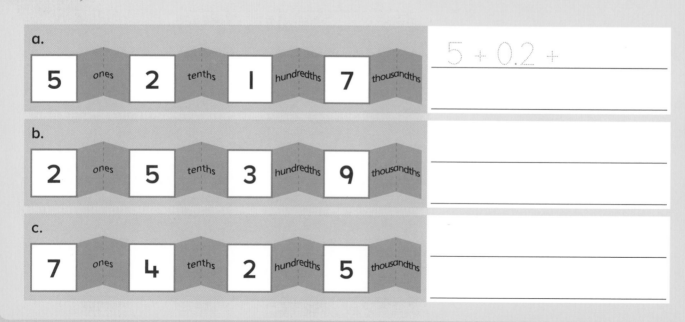

a.

| 5 | ones | 2 | tenths | 1 | hundredths | 7 | thousandths |

$5 + 0.2 + $ ____

b.

| 2 | ones | 5 | tenths | 3 | hundredths | 9 | thousandths |

____

c.

| 7 | ones | 4 | tenths | 2 | hundredths | 5 | thousandths |

____

2. Write an expression that uses decimal fractions to show the parts of these numbers.

a.

b.

c.

d.

3. Write an expression that uses common fractions to break each decimal fraction into parts. The first example has been done for you.

a.

$$5 + \frac{3}{10} + \frac{2}{100} + \frac{6}{1000}$$

b.

c.

d.

Step Ahead For each of these, color the ⬭ beside the statement that is true.

a.

is the same as

◯ 53 tenths + 26 hundredths

◯ 532 hundredths + 6 thousandths

◯ 5 ones + 326 tenths

b.

 is the same as

◯ 208 hundredths + 3 thousandths

◯ 20 tenths + 83 hundredths

◯ 208 tenths + 3 thousandths

A room at the Seasons Hotel costs \$132 for one night.

About how much is the total cost for 3 nights?

How would you figure out the exact cost?

	1	3	2
×			3
			6
		9	0
	3	0	0

Felix multiplied the parts to figure out the total cost.

What steps did he follow?

What is the total cost? How do you know?

Write the total cost in the empty boxes.

Isabelle used the standard algorithm for multiplication to calculate the total cost. She followed these steps.

Step 1	Step 2	Step 3

H	T	O
1	3	2
×		3
		6

H	T	O
1	3	2
×		3
	9	6

H	T	O
1	3	2
×		3
3	9	6

What numbers did she multiply in each step?

Compare the two methods above. How are they the same? How are they different?

How could you use Isabelle's method to calculate 2,312 × 3?

Step Up

1. Estimate each product. Then use the standard multiplication algorithm to calculate the exact answer.

a. Estimate

H	T	O
3	1	2
×		3

b. Estimate

H	T	O
4	2	4
×		2

c. Estimate

H	T	O
2	1	2
×		4

d. Estimate

H	T	O
1	3	1
×		3

2. Complete each of these.

a. Estimate

H	T	O
I	0	3
×		3

b. Estimate

H	T	O
3	4	I
×		2

c. Estimate

H	T	O
I	2	3
×		3

d. Estimate

H	T	O
2	I	0
×		4

e. Estimate

Th	H	T	O
I	3	I	2
×			3

f. Estimate

Th	H	T	O
2	4	4	I
×			2

g. Estimate

Th	H	T	O
I	0	I	2
×			4

h. Estimate

Th	H	T	O
3	I	2	3
×			3

i. Estimate

Th	H	T	O
3	0	3	I
×			3

j. Estimate

Th	H	T	O
I	I	0	2
×			4

k. Estimate

Th	H	T	O
2	4	3	0
×			2

l. Estimate

Th	H	T	O
3	2	0	2
×			3

Step Ahead Look at each card below. Draw a ✔ on the card that shows partial products that match this standard multiplication algorithm.

	2	3	I	3
×				3
	6	9	3	9

| $3 \times 3 = 9$ |
| $1 \times 3 = 3$ |
| $3 \times 3 = 9$ |
| $2 \times 3 = 6$ |

| $3 \times 3 = 9$ |
| $10 \times 3 = 30$ |
| $300 \times 3 = 900$ |
| $2,000 \times 3 = 6,000$ |

| $3 \times 3 = 9$ |
| $10 \times 3 = 30$ |
| $30 \times 3 = 90$ |
| $200 \times 3 = 600$ |

About how much is the total cost of three of these monitors?

How could you figure out the exact cost?

Mato figured it out like this. What steps did he follow?

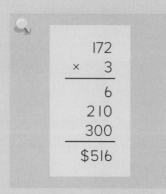

$$
\begin{array}{r}
172 \\
\times \quad 3 \\
\hline
6 \\
210 \\
300 \\
\hline
\$516 \\
\end{array}
$$

What other methods could you use?

Eva used the standard multiplication algorithm.

Step 1		
H	T	O
1	7	2
×		3
		6

Step 2		
	2	
H	T	O
1	7	2
×		3
	1	6

Step 3		
	2	
H	T	O
1	7	2
×		3
5	1	6

What numbers did she multiply in each step?

What does the red digit in the hundreds place represent?

How did she use this digit?

Compare the two methods above.
How are they the same? How are they different?

How could you use Eva's method to calculate 3,261 × 4?

Write your estimate. Then use the standard multiplication algorithm to calculate the exact product.

a. Estimate
_____

H	T	O
4	2	6
×		3

b. Estimate
_____

H	T	O
3	7	5
×		5

c. Estimate
_____

H	T	O
6	4	2
×		4

d. Estimate
_____

H	T	O
5	2	8
×		7

e. Estimate
_____

H	T	O
5	8	0
×		4

f. Estimate
_____

H	T	O
7	5	3
×		6

g. Estimate
_____

H	T	O
3	0	9
×		8

h. Estimate
_____

H	T	O
9	1	9
×		3

i. Estimate
_____

Th	H	T	O
3	4	2	5
×			3

j. Estimate
_____

Th	H	T	O
5	7	9	1
×			6

k. Estimate
_____

Th	H	T	O
4	0	3	9
×			4

Write the correct answer. Then describe the mistake in words.

	⁴	⁵	
	6	0	7
×			8
5	2	0	6

_____

_____

_____

Using the Standard Algorithm to Multiply Two Two-Digit Numbers

A school hall has a rectangular floor. The dimensions are 24 yd × 32 yd.

How would you estimate the area of the floor?

How could you figure out the exact area?

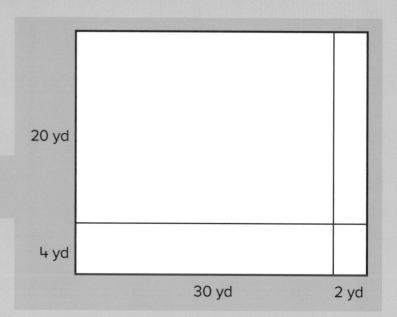

20 yd

4 yd

30 yd   2 yd

Corey drew this diagram. How will it help him figure out the area of the floor?

Write the partial product inside each part of the diagram.

What is the area? How do you know?

Mia used the standard multiplication algorithm to calculate the exact area.

Step 1	Step 2	Step 3	Step 4	Step 5
H T O	H T O	H T O	H T O	H T O
2 4	2 4	¹ 2 4	¹ 2 4	¹ 2 4
× 3 2	× 3 2	× 3 2	× 3 2	× 3 2
8	4 8	4 8	4 8	4 8
		2 0	7 2 0	7 2 0
				7 6 8

Does it matter which factor is written in the top row? How do you know?
What numbers did she multiply in each step?

Compare the partial-products method and the standard algorithm. How are they similar?

Look carefully at the numbers being multiplied in each step of the algorithm.
Where are the matching partial products in Corey's diagram?

What is another way you could figure out the area?

I would break the rectangle into two parts. That's 24 x 3 tens plus 24 x 2.

A builder made some quick calculations. Make an estimate, then check each calculation and mark it with a ✔ or a ✘. If it is not correct, write the correct calculation to the side.

a.
```
    39
  ×  41
    39
   156
   195
```

b.
```
    29
  ×  31
    29
   870
   899
```

c.
```
    26
  ×  35
   130
   780
   910
```

d.
```
    70
  ×  61
    70
  3600
  3670
```

e.
```
    53
  ×  27
   371
  1060
  1431
```

f.
```
    39
  ×  62
    78
   234
   302
```

Step Ahead

Look at the algorithm that Mia used on page 60. Explain why she wrote a zero in the ones place in Step 3.

_____

_____

_____

Using the Standard Algorithm to Multiply Three- and Two-Digit Numbers

A ferry seats 132 people. It makes 24 trips each day.

Does the ferry carry more or less than 2,500 people each day?

How could you figure out the exact number?

Logan drew this diagram to figure out the exact number.

How will it help him?

Write the partial products inside each part of the diagram.

	20	4
100		
30		
2		

Paige used the standard multiplication algorithm to calculate the total.

How did she calculate the number in the first row?
What does the red digit in the hundreds place represent?

What numbers should she write in the second row?
Write numbers to show your thinking. Then write the total.

What is the total number of passengers that could travel on the ferry each day?

		1	3	2
×			2	4
		5	2	8

Step Up

1. Write the partial product inside each part of the diagram below.
   Then add these to calculate the area.

$32 \times 145 =$ _____

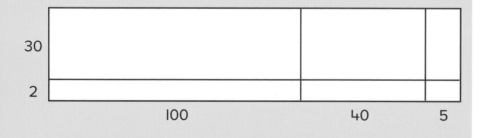

2. Use the standard multiplication algorithm to calculate the exact product.
Then estimate the product to check that your answer makes sense.

a.
```
    1  4  2
×      2  1
```

b.
```
    6  7  5
×      4  2
```

c.
```
    2  1  4
×      4  2
```

d.
```
    1  7  3
×      3  2
```

e.
```
    3  2  9
×      5  4
```

f.
```
    2  0  8
×      7  3
```

Step Ahead

Look at this calculation.
Describe the mistake in words.

		1	4	6
×			5	4
		5	8	4
		7	3	0
	1	3	1	4

3.5 Extending the Standard Multiplication Algorithm

The local park is rectangular and measures 134 yd by 232 yd.

How could you figure out the area of the park?

Maka drew this diagram of a rectangle split into parts to make it easier to multiply.

Write the partial product inside each part of her diagram.

Add the partial products in your head and write the area of the park below.

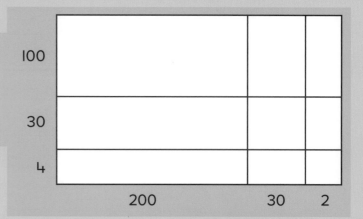

Area is _____ yd²

Noah used the standard multiplication algorithm to calculate the area. What steps did he follow?

Look carefully at the first and third row of his calculations. What do you notice?

Why is the product in the third row 100 times greater than the product in the first row?

```
      1 1
      1 3 4
  ×   2 3 2
  1   2 6 8
1 4   0 2 0
2 6   8 0 0
3 1   0 8 8
```

Step Up

I. Write the partial product inside each part of the diagram below. Then add these to calculate the area.

153 × 328 = _____

2. Use the standard multiplication algorithm to calculate the exact product.
Then estimate the product to check that your answer makes sense.

a.

```
    1  3  4  2
 ×        1  2
 ─────────────
```

b.

```
       5  8  7
 ×     4  2  0
 ─────────────
```

c.

```
       1  6  1
 ×     2  5  1
 ─────────────
```

d.

```
    1  0  4  2
 ×        3  2  1
 ─────────────
```

e.

```
       4  2  7
 ×     2  0  5
 ─────────────
```

f.

```
    3  5  2  6
 ×        2  3  5
 ─────────────
```

Step Ahead   Color the ⬭ beside the estimate that you think is closest to the exact product.

a.   127 × 53

- ⬭ 600
- ⬭ 6,000
- ⬭ 60,000
- ⬭ 600,000

b.   7,325 × 49

- ⬭ 35,000
- ⬭ 13,500
- ⬭ 350,000
- ⬭ 280,000

c.   308 × 426

- ⬭ 12,000
- ⬭ 120,000
- ⬭ 1,200
- ⬭ 13,000

d.   6,097 × 720

- ⬭ 42,000
- ⬭ 4,200,000
- ⬭ 420,000
- ⬭ 460,000

3.6 Solving Word Problems Involving Multiplication

This table shows the payments that players received after each game and the number of games that they played.

Player	Payment	Games Played
A	$4,350	4
B	$1,025	5
C	$895	11
D	$12,352	32
E	$20,499	18

How could you figure out the total amount that Player A received?

Dana used the standard algorithm to multiply like this.

```
    1 2
  4 3 5 0
×       4
─────────
1 7 4 0 0
```

Jose used a doubling strategy.

Double 4,350 = 8,700

Double 8,700 = 17,400

How would you figure out the total amount that Player B received?

Step Up

1. Look at the table above. Figure out the total amount paid to each of these players.

Player C	Player D	Player E
$ _____	$ _____	$ _____

2. Solve these word problems. Show your thinking.

a. It costs $895 to replace a backboard. 12 backboards were replaced in one season. What is the total cost of replacing them?

$ _____

b. It costs $7,320 to use the stadium for each game. What is the total cost to use the stadium for 41 games?

$ _____

c. There are 28 seats in each row. There are 42 rows. What is the total number of seats in the stand?

_____ seats

d. Membership costs $245 a season. There are 4,043 members. How much money is paid to the club for memberships?

$ _____

Step Ahead

Look at the table at the top of page 66. There are 82 regular games in one season. Estimate the amount that each player below would earn if they played every game. Then use a calculator to check your estimates.

Player A	Player B	Player C	Player D
$ _____	$ _____	$ _____	$ _____

Place base-10 ones blocks on this base picture so it is six layers high.

How can you figure out how many ones blocks you used?

Complete this table to help you. What do you notice?

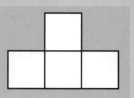

Number of cubes in base	Number of layers	Total number of cubes
4	1	4
4	2	8
4	3	
4		
4		
4		

The total number of cubes tells you the volume of the object.

How could you quickly figure out the total number of cubes in any object?

What do you need to know?

Volume is the amount of space that an object occupies.

Step Up

1. Place base-10 ones blocks on this base picture. Build up the number of layers to match the data in the table. Then complete the table.

Number of cubes in base	Number of layers	Total number of cubes
6	1	6
6	2	12
6	3	
6	4	

2. Complete these tables. You can use ones blocks to help.

a.

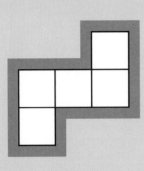

Number of cubes in base	Number of layers	Total number of cubes
5	1	
	2	
	3	
	4	

b.

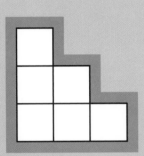

Number of cubes in base	Number of layers	Total number of cubes
6	1	
	3	
	5	
	7	

c.

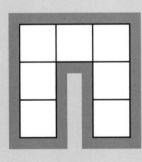

Number of cubes in base	Number of layers	Total number of cubes
7	2	
	4	
	6	
	8	

Step Ahead

1. Use 32 ones blocks to make an object that is the same on each layer. Draw the base of your object.

2. Write the missing numbers.

a. Number of blocks in base _____

b. Number of layers _____

Analyzing Unit Cubes and Measuring Volume

Layla was storing these boxes in the garage.

How can she compare the amount of space that each box will occupy?

To measure the space, she decides to fill each box with objects that are the same shape. How will this help?

Look at these objects.

Which object would you use to measure the volume of each box?

How did you decide?

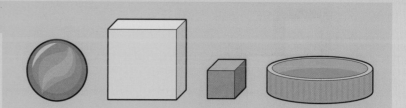

Layla chose to use centimeter cubes to find the volume of the jewelery box.

Does she need to fill the whole box with cubes?

What is an easier way to figure out the volume?

Just find the number of cubes in one layer. Then find the number of layers.

Step Up

I. Use base-10 ones blocks to cover the area of this rectangle. Then complete the table.

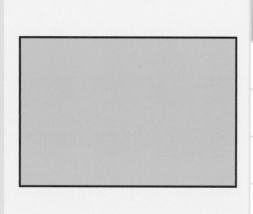

Dimensions of the base of the prism (cm)	Number of layers	Total number of centimeter cubes
×	1	
×	2	
×	3	
×	4	

2. Use base-10 ones blocks to cover the area of this rectangle. Then complete the table.

Dimensions of the base of the prism (cm)	Number of layers	Total number of centimeter cubes
×	1	
×	2	
×	3	
×	5	

3. Complete each table to show the total number of centimeter cubes in each prism.

Dimensions of the base (cm)	Number of layers	Total number of centimeter cubes
4 × 5	1	
4 × 5	2	
4 × 5	3	
4 × 5	5	
4 × 5	8	

Dimensions of the base (cm)	Number of layers	Total number of centimeter cubes
8 × 3	1	
8 × 3	2	
8 × 3	4	
8 × 3	5	
8 × 3	10	

4. Write a rule to figure out the total number of cubes in a prism when you know the dimensions of the base and the number of layers. Use your answers in Question 3 to help.

Step Ahead Tyler pours cubes into this container to figure out the volume. He counts 58 cubes. Do you think his calculation is accurate? Explain your thinking.

3.9　Developing a Formula to Calculate Volume

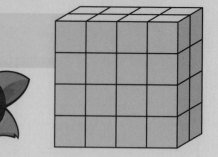

How can you figure out the volume of this prism without counting each individual cube?

I know there are 8 cubes in the base. There are 4 layers. 8 + 8 + 8 + 8 = 32.

Cody multiplied the height of the prism by the number of cubes in the base.

Base	Height
8 cubes	4 layers

$8 \times 4 = 32$ cubes
Volume is 32 cubes.

Lara multiplied the dimensions.

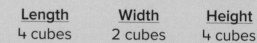

Length	Width	Height
4 cubes	2 cubes	4 cubes

$4 \times 2 \times 4 = 32$ cubes
Volume is 32 cubes.

How are their methods similar?

What rule could you write to match each method?

Look at Lara's method.

Does it matter in what order she multiplies the dimensions? How do you know?

Volume is usually measured in cubic units. The abbreviation for cubic centimeters is cm^3.

Step Up

1. Imagine you built this prism with base-10 ones blocks.

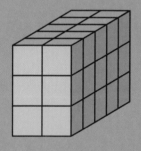

   a. Complete this table.

Length (blocks)	Width (blocks)	Height (blocks)	Total number of blocks

   b. Write the volume of the prism. cm^3

2. Here are the dimensions of another prism.

   Length 8 cm   Width 3 cm   Height 5 cm

   Write how you can calculate the volume without counting blocks.

   _____

3. Use your rule from Question 2 to calculate the volume of these prisms.

	Length (cm)	Width (cm)	Height (cm)	Volume (cm³)
a.	5	4	3	
b.	9	6	4	
c.	7	5	5	
d.	7	6	3	

4. Calculate the volume of each prism.
Then write an equation to show the order that you multiplied the dimensions.

a.
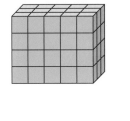

_____ cm³

b.
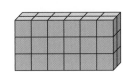

_____ cm³

c.
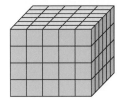

_____ cm³

Step Ahead

This square-based pyramid has been built with base-10 ones blocks.

Calculate the volume of the pyramid.

_____ cm³

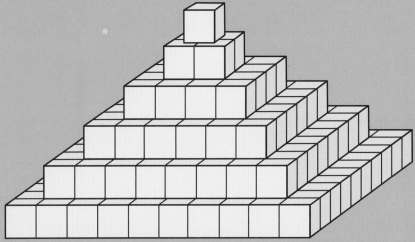

The volume of a box is 60 in³. Write some possible dimensions for the box.

| ☐ × ☐ × ☐ = 60 in³ | ☐ × ☐ × ☐ = 60 in³ | ☐ × ☐ × ☐ = 60 in³ |

How did you figure out the dimensions?

What do you notice about each of the dimensions?

> Each dimension is a factor of 60.
> 60 has a lot of factors.

How many different prisms can you make from a number that is prime?

How do you know?

Step Up

1. For each of these, draw and label the dimensions of a prism to match. Then write the volume.

a.	just less than 80 in³

_____ in³

b.	just more than 80 in³

_____ in³

c.	just less than 55 in³

_____ in³

d.	just more than 55 in³

_____ in³

2. Complete each table to show the dimensions of four different prisms that have the same volume.

a.	Volume is 36 in³	
Length	Width	Height

b.	Volume is 64 in³	
Length	Width	Height

c.	Volume is 100 in³	
Length	Width	Height

d.	Volume is 72 in³	
Length	Width	Height

3. Write the dimensions for another prism that has the same volume as 4 cm × 8 cm × 10 cm.

Length _____ cm   Width _____ cm   Height _____ cm

Step Ahead

Prism A is made with inch cubes. It is 4 cubes long, 5 cubes wide, and 2 cubes high. Prism B is made with centimeter cubes. It is 6 cubes long, 2 cubes wide, and 4 cubes high.

Which prism has the **greater volume**? Explain your thinking.

_____
_____
_____

Working with Volume

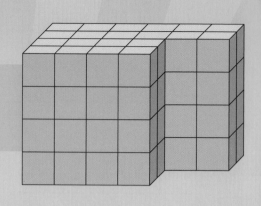

The base of this prism has **6** sides.
It is called a hexagonal-based prism.

How could you calculate the volume of this prism?

Julia split the prism into two rectangular-based prisms.

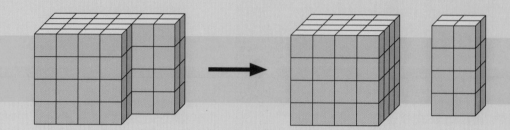

How will breaking the prism into parts help her figure out the volume?

What number sentences would you write to match?

Jacob used a different strategy. He added more blocks to change the hexagonal-based prism into a rectangular-based prism.

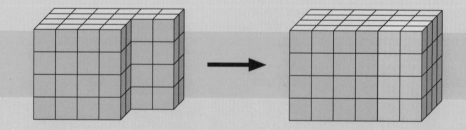

How could Jacob's strategy help him figure out the volume of the prism?

What number sentences would you write to match?

Step Up

1. Each of these small cubes is I cm³. Figure out the volume of the prism. Write number sentences to show your thinking.

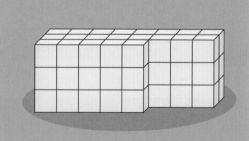

_____ cm³

2. These prisms are made with centimeter cubes. Figure out the volume of each prism.
   Show your thinking.

a.

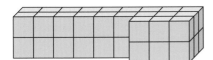

_____ cm³

b.

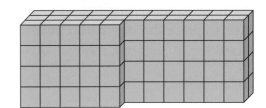

_____ cm³

c.

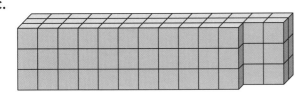

_____ cm³

d.

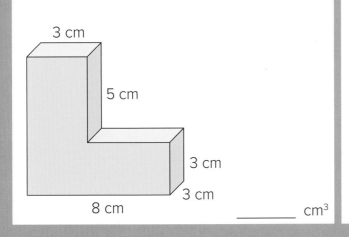

3 cm

5 cm

3 cm

3 cm

8 cm

_____ cm³

e.

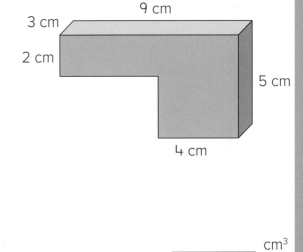

9 cm

3 cm

2 cm

5 cm

4 cm

_____ cm³

Step Ahead

Some centimeter cubes have been removed from the middle of this prism.
Figure out the volume of the new object.

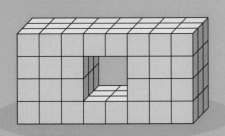

_____ cm³

Solving Word Problems Involving Volume

Janice is moving some household items into storage.
She decides to pack the items into boxes.
Boxes are sold in these three sizes.

What is the volume
of each box?
How do you know?

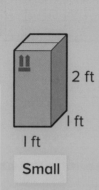

2 ft
1 ft
1 ft

Small

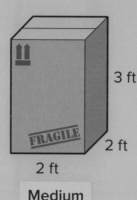

3 ft
2 ft
2 ft

FRAGILE

Medium

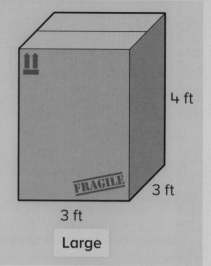

4 ft
3 ft
3 ft

FRAGILE

Large

Janice rents some storage space with the dimensions 10 ft × 10 ft × 8 ft.
What is the volume of the storage space?

She buys and fills 5 large boxes and 5 medium boxes.
How much space do the boxes occupy in storage?

How much storage space does she have left?

Think about the dimensions of the boxes and the dimensions of the storage space.

What size box would you use to fill the storage space? Why?

The height of the storage space is 8 feet so there would
be some space left over if I used the medium boxes.

Step Up

1. Use the box sizes above. Figure out the total volume that each group of boxes would occupy.

a.	2 large boxes 3 medium boxes	b.	4 large boxes 7 small boxes	c.	3 large boxes 2 medium boxes 6 small boxes

_____ ft³   _____ ft³   _____ ft³

2. Use the box sizes shown on page 78 to solve these word problems. Show your thinking.

a. Lilly buys and fills 4 boxes of each size. What is the total volume of the boxes?

_____ ft³

b. Mika has 5 medium boxes in the attic and 2 large boxes in the basement. Which group of boxes has the greater volume?

_____

c. Kimie's storage space measures 8 ft × 8 ft × 10 ft. What is the greatest number of full large boxes she can put in this storage space?

_____ large boxes

d. James has a storage space that measures 9 ft × 9 ft × 9 ft. What is the greatest number of medium boxes he can pack into this space?

_____ medium boxes

Step Ahead

Look at Question 2c above. After Kimie packs the large boxes into storage, how much space will be left over?

_____ ft³

Reviewing Addition of Common Fractions and Mixed Numbers (Same Denominators)

This picture shows two wholes.
Use pattern blocks of the same color
to cover these shapes to show $\frac{4}{3}$.

Complete this equation to match the amount
uncovered and the total amount covered.

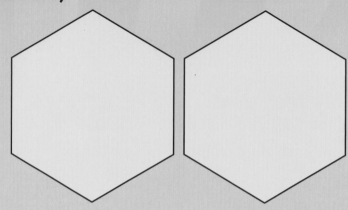

$$\frac{4}{3} + \boxed{} = \boxed{}$$

Why is the total the same as 2?

Write two common fractions with the same denominator that make
this equation true. You can use red or blue or green pattern blocks
and cover parts of the shapes above to help.

$$2 = \boxed{} + \boxed{}$$

What are some different equations you could write so that you still have a sum of 2?

Imagine you covered the hexagons with green pattern blocks.
Now imagine you had four extra green pattern blocks.

How would you write the total using mixed numbers? $\boxed{}$

Use mixed numbers to write an equation that has the same total.

$$\boxed{} = \boxed{} + \boxed{}$$

Step Up

1. Write fractions to complete true equations. The fractions in each equation
should have the same denominators. You can use the number line to help.

a. $\dfrac{5}{4} = \boxed{} + \boxed{}$

b. $2\dfrac{1}{4} = \boxed{} + \boxed{}$

c. $3\dfrac{3}{4} = \boxed{} + \boxed{}$

```
 |---|---|---|---|---|---|---|---|---|---|---|---|--->
 0               1               2               3
```

d. $\dfrac{5}{3} = \boxed{} + \boxed{}$

e. $2\dfrac{2}{3} = \boxed{} + \boxed{}$

f. $1\dfrac{1}{3} = \boxed{} + \boxed{}$

2. Write the total amount of the ingredients as a common fraction or mixed number. Show your thinking.

Corn Muffins

$\frac{1}{4}$ cup oil

$1\frac{1}{4}$ cups cornmeal

$\frac{1}{4}$ cup canned corn

$\frac{3}{4}$ cup flour

I cup milk

I egg

a. oil, flour, and canned corn

☐ cups

b. cornmeal, milk, and oil

☐ cups

Apple Oatmeal

$\frac{1}{3}$ cup apple juice

$\frac{2}{3}$ cup water

$\frac{2}{3}$ cup oats

cinnamon to taste

c. apple juice, water, and oats

☐ cups

Apple Muffins

$1\frac{1}{4}$ cups finely chopped apples

$\frac{1}{4}$ cup walnuts

$2\frac{1}{4}$ cups flour

$\frac{1}{4}$ cup milk

I egg

d. apples, walnuts, and milk

☐ cups

e. apples and flour

☐ cups

Step Ahead In a magic square, the numbers in each row, column, and diagonal have the same total which is called the magic number.

These are fraction magic squares. The fractions in each square have the same denominators. Figure out and write the magic number. Then write fractions to complete each square.

a.

$\frac{8}{3}$		
	$\frac{5}{3}$	$\frac{7}{3}$
		$\frac{2}{3}$

The magic number is ☐

b.

$\frac{2}{4}$		
$\frac{9}{4}$	$\frac{5}{4}$	$\frac{1}{4}$

The magic number is ☐

Adding Common Fractions (Related Denominators)

These pizzas were left over after a party.

Very Veggie

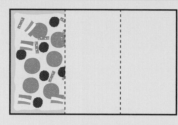
Mostly Meat

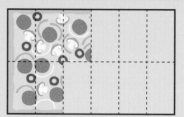
Super Supreme

Choose two types of pizza to take home. What are the possible combinations you could choose?

What number sentence could you write to show how to figure out the total for each combination?

Which combinations of leftover pizzas match these equations?

$\dfrac{1}{3} + \dfrac{1}{6} = $ ⬚

$\dfrac{5}{12} + \dfrac{1}{6} = $ ⬚

$\dfrac{1}{3} + \dfrac{5}{12} = $ ⬚

What do you notice about the denominators in each pair?
How would you figure out the total?

I can see that the denominator 12 is a multiple of the denominator 3.

Step Up

1. For each of these, rewrite the equation so the denominators are the same. Use the number line to help. Then write the total.

a. $\dfrac{2}{5} + \dfrac{1}{10} = $ ⬚

b. $\dfrac{3}{20} + \dfrac{3}{5} = $ ⬚

c. $\dfrac{3}{10} + \dfrac{5}{5} = $ ⬚

2. Rewrite each equation so the denominators are the same. Then write the total.

a.
$$\frac{1}{3} + \frac{5}{9} = \boxed{\frac{}{}}$$

b.
$$\frac{5}{8} + \frac{3}{16} = \boxed{\frac{}{}}$$

c.
$$\frac{2}{3} + \frac{2}{15} = \boxed{\frac{}{}}$$

d.
$$\frac{1}{4} + \frac{7}{16} = \boxed{\frac{}{}}$$

e.
$$\frac{5}{20} + \frac{1}{4} = \boxed{\frac{}{}}$$

f.
$$\frac{3}{12} + \frac{2}{3} = \boxed{\frac{}{}}$$

3. Color the ⬭ beside the best description of the total. Show how you decided.

a.
$$\frac{1}{2} + \frac{1}{4} + \frac{1}{8}$$
- ◯ more than 1
- ◯ equal to 1
- ◯ less than 1

b.
$$\frac{1}{2} + \frac{1}{3} + \frac{1}{6}$$
- ◯ more than 1
- ◯ equal to 1
- ◯ less than 1

Step Ahead

The Ancient Egyptians only had symbols for unit fractions. So when they wanted to write a fraction such as $\frac{5}{8}$, they wrote $\frac{1}{2} + \frac{1}{8}$ (two unit fractions). They always used the fewest number of unit fractions needed. What single or sum of unit fractions would they have used for each of these? The first two have been done for you.

$$\frac{1}{8} = \frac{1}{\boxed{8}} \qquad \frac{2}{8} = \frac{1}{\boxed{4}} \qquad \frac{6}{8} = \boxed{} \qquad \frac{9}{8} = \boxed{}$$

Adding Common Fractions (Unrelated Denominators)

These pizzas were left over after a party.

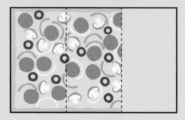

Serious Supreme

Cheese and Cheese

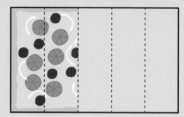

Tasty Tomato

Choose two types of pizza to take home. What are the possible combinations you could choose?

What equation would you write to show how to figure out the total for each combination?

| | = ? | | = ? | | = ? |

What do you notice about the denominators of the fractions?

How would you complete each sentence below? How did you decide?

The common denominator for thirds and fourths is _____.

The common denominator for fourths and fifths is _____.

The common denominator for thirds and fifths is _____.

How would you figure out the total for each equation you wrote above?

Step Up

I. For each of these, write the denominator that is common to both fractions and complete the equivalent fractions. Then write the totals.

a.
$$\frac{2}{3} + \frac{1}{4} = \boxed{}$$

$$\boxed{} + \boxed{} = \boxed{}$$

b.
$$\frac{2}{5} + \frac{1}{4} = \boxed{}$$

$$\boxed{} + \boxed{} = \boxed{}$$

c.
$$\frac{2}{3} + \frac{2}{5} = \boxed{}$$

$$\boxed{} + \boxed{} = \boxed{}$$

2. Rewrite both fractions so they have the same denominators. Then write the total.

a.

$$\frac{1}{3} + \frac{3}{5} = \frac{}{}$$

b.

$$\frac{2}{3} + \frac{3}{8} = \frac{}{}$$

c.

$$\frac{3}{5} + \frac{1}{12} = \frac{}{}$$

d.

$$\frac{1}{4} + \frac{1}{6} = \frac{}{}$$

e.

$$\frac{3}{8} + \frac{1}{3} = \frac{}{}$$

f.

$$\frac{3}{12} + \frac{3}{8} = \frac{}{}$$

3. Color the ◯ beside the best description of the total. Show how you decided.

a.

$$\frac{1}{2} + \frac{1}{3} + \frac{1}{4}$$

◯ more than 1
◯ equal to 1
◯ less than 1

b.

$$\frac{1}{2} + \frac{1}{4} + \frac{1}{5}$$

◯ more than 1
◯ equal to 1
◯ less than 1

Step Ahead

Remember the Ancient Egyptians only had symbols for unit fractions. They always used one or a sum of unit fractions to write any fraction and they tried to use the fewest number of unit fractions.

How would the Ancient Egyptians have written these fractions? The first one has been done for you.

$$\frac{1}{12} = \frac{1}{12}$$

$$\frac{4}{12} = \frac{}{}$$

$$\frac{8}{12} = $$

$$\frac{11}{12} = $$

4.4 ▶ Adding Mixed Numbers (Related Denominators)

Manuel bought these two strips of wood for a picture frame.

$5\frac{1}{4}$ feet

$7\frac{1}{2}$ feet

How would you figure out the total length of both strips?

Look at these students' methods.

Nadie thought it would be easier to add the lengths using improper fractions. This is what she wrote.	Brady added the whole numbers and then the fractions.	Claire added by writing one mixed number below the other.
$\frac{15}{2} + \frac{21}{4} = \boxed{}$	$7 + 5 + \frac{1}{2} + \frac{1}{4}$	$7\frac{1}{2}$ $+\ 5\frac{1}{4}$ ———

Before they add, what will they need to do with the fractions?

How do you think they will figure out the total?

Step Up ▶

I. Show how you would figure out each total in two ways. One way should use improper fractions. The second method should use mixed numbers.

a.	Use improper fractions	Use mixed numbers
$3\frac{1}{4} + 2\frac{3}{8}$		

b.	Use improper fractions	Use mixed numbers
$4\frac{1}{3} + 2\frac{5}{12}$		

2. Figure out the totals using improper fractions and then mixed numbers.

a.

$1\frac{4}{15} + 4\frac{2}{5}$

Use improper fractions	Use mixed numbers

b.

$2\frac{3}{8} + 1\frac{5}{24}$

Use improper fractions	Use mixed numbers

3. Look at this picture frame.

a. Show how you could figure out the total of the two strips used for the **longer side** of the frame.

$2\frac{3}{8}$ ft

$3\frac{1}{2}$ ft

b. Show how you could figure out the total of the two strips used for the **shorter side** of the frame.

Step Ahead

Figure out the perimeter of the picture frame shown in Question 3. Show your thinking.

_____ ft

Adding Mixed Numbers (Unrelated Denominators)

How could you figure out the total amount of juice
and water in this apple cake recipe?

Apple Cake

$1\frac{2}{3}$ cups apple juice

$1\frac{1}{4}$ cups water

$1\frac{1}{3}$ cups oats

$1\frac{1}{2}$ cups flour

Carter changed the amounts
to improper fractions to add.

$$\frac{5}{3} + \frac{5}{4} = \boxed{}$$

Emily used the mixed numbers.

$$1\frac{2}{3} + 1\frac{1}{4} = \boxed{}$$

What will Carter and Emily need to do before they can add?

How should Carter rewrite the fractions to add?
What steps will he follow to figure out the total?

How should Emily rewrite the fractions to add?
What steps could Emily follow to add the mixed numbers?
What different ways could Emily figure out the total?

How would you check that the total in Carter's
method is the same as the total in Emily's method?

Step Up

I. Show how you would figure out each total in two ways. One way should use
improper fractions. The second method should use mixed numbers.

a.	Use improper fractions	Use mixed numbers
$1\frac{1}{4} + 2\frac{1}{3}$		

b.	Use improper fractions	Use mixed numbers
$2\frac{1}{3} + 3\frac{2}{5}$		

2. Figure out the totals using improper fractions and then mixed numbers.

a.	Use improper fractions	Use mixed numbers
$2\frac{3}{5} + 3\frac{1}{4}$		

b.	Use improper fractions	Use mixed numbers
$3\frac{3}{4} + 2\frac{1}{6}$		

3. Figure out the total distance between these towns.
Use a method of your choice.

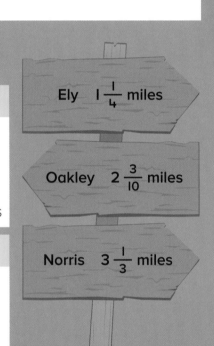

Ely $1\frac{1}{4}$ miles

Oakley $2\frac{3}{10}$ miles

Norris $3\frac{1}{3}$ miles

a.	Oakley to Ely
	_____ miles

b.	Norris to Oakley
	_____ miles

Step Ahead
Read the clues. Complete the signs to match the clues using numbers of your choice for Parkes and Tipton.

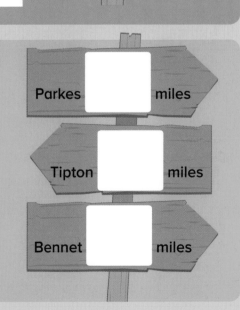

Parkes ☐ miles

Tipton ☐ miles

Bennet ☐ miles

CLUES

• The total distance from Parkes to Tipton is 5 miles.

• Bennet is $2\frac{1}{5}$ miles farther away from Tipton than from Parkes.

• All distances are mixed numbers with different denominators.

Adding Mixed Numbers (Unrelated Denominators and Composing Whole Numbers)

How would you figure out the total of these two amounts?

What steps could you use?

$1\frac{2}{3}$ cups $1\frac{3}{4}$ cups

The fraction part of both numbers has to be rewritten before you can add.

Write the missing numerators.

$$1\frac{2}{3} + 1\frac{3}{4} = 1\frac{}{12} + 1\frac{}{12} = \boxed{}$$

Sofia added the whole numbers first.
Draw jumps on this number line to show how she could have figured out the total.

Jamal added the fractions first.
Draw jumps on this number line to show how he could have figured out the total.

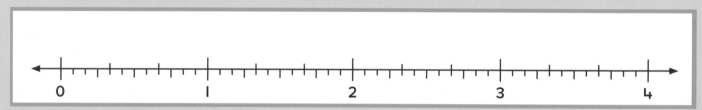

Jamal added the fractions like this.
What did he do with the improper fraction to find the total?

$$1 + 1 + \frac{17}{12} = 1 + 1 + 1 + \frac{5}{12}$$

Step Up

1. For each of these, rewrite the mixed numbers so the fractions have the same denominators. Then show how you add to calculate the total.

a.	Same denominators	Show addition
$1\frac{2}{3} + 1\frac{3}{4}$		

b.	Same denominators	Show addition
$2\frac{2}{3} + 1\frac{3}{5}$		

2. Rewrite each of these so the fractions have the same denominators.
Then show how you calculate the total.

a.	Same denominators	Show addition
$1\frac{5}{6} + 2\frac{3}{4}$		

b.	Same denominators	Show addition
$2\frac{5}{6} + 1\frac{3}{8}$		

3. Is the total amount in each group of three containers **more** or **less** than four cups?
Show your thinking.

a.

_____ than 4 cups

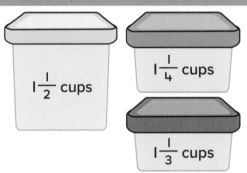

b.

_____ than 4 cups

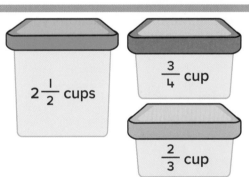

Step Ahead

Write different mixed numbers to make each equation true.
Make the denominators of the fractions different.

a.

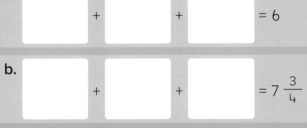

$\boxed{} + \boxed{} + \boxed{} = 6$

b.

$\boxed{} + \boxed{} + \boxed{} = 7\frac{3}{4}$

Working Space

Adding Common Fractions and Mixed Numbers (Unrelated Denominators)

This fraction game was designed by fifth grade students.
The fractions are written on the faces of two blank cubes.
Then both cubes are rolled and the fractions are added.

This table shows the scores for each pair of denominators.

Fractions Over/Under

Cube A		
$\frac{1}{3}$	$\frac{4}{6}$	$\frac{7}{9}$
$\frac{10}{12}$	$\frac{13}{15}$	$\frac{16}{18}$

Cube B		
$\frac{3}{2}$	$\frac{5}{4}$	$\frac{7}{6}$
$\frac{9}{8}$	$\frac{11}{10}$	$\frac{13}{12}$

Points for denominators

- 0 points if the denominators are the same.
- 1 point if one denominator must be changed to add.
- 2 points if both denominators must be changed to add.

What are some pairs of fractions that would earn 1 point?

What are some pairs of fractions that would earn 2 points?

This table shows the scores for each total.

Points for totals

- 1 point if the sum is less than two.
- 2 points if the sum is greater than two.

What are some pairs of fractions you could roll that will have a total less than 2?

What are some pairs of fractions you could roll that will have a total greater than two?

Step Up

1. Look at the ways of scoring points above. Figure out the total number of points that you would make for each of these rolls. Show your thinking.

a.

Total score _____

b.

Total score _____

c.

Total score _____

Another game is called *Mixed Numbers Over/Under.* It is played in the same way as the game described at the top of page 92. Points are scored for the denominators and for the total.

Points for denominators	Points for totals
• I point if one denominator must be changed.	• I point if the sum is less than three.
• 2 points if both denominators must be changed.	• 2 points if the sum is greater than three.

2. Read how to score points in the game above. Then figure out the total number of points that you would make for each of these rolls. Show your thinking.

a. $1\frac{2}{3}$ $1\frac{1}{2}$

Total score _____

b. $1\frac{1}{6}$ $1\frac{3}{4}$

Total score _____

c. $1\frac{1}{5}$ $1\frac{5}{6}$

Total score _____

d. $1\frac{4}{5}$ $1\frac{1}{2}$

Total score _____

Step Ahead

The chart shows the cubes used to play *Mixed Numbers Over/Under.*

Estimate three rolls of the cubes that will each make a total very close to 3. Write your estimates below. Then check which of the rolls is closest to 3. You can make notes on scrap paper.

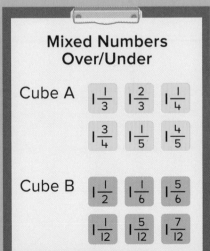

Mixed Numbers Over/Under

Cube A $1\frac{1}{3}$ $1\frac{2}{3}$ $1\frac{1}{4}$ $1\frac{3}{4}$ $1\frac{1}{5}$ $1\frac{4}{5}$

Cube B $1\frac{1}{2}$ $1\frac{1}{6}$ $1\frac{5}{6}$ $1\frac{1}{12}$ $1\frac{5}{12}$ $1\frac{7}{12}$

Solving Multi-Step Word Problems Involving Mixed Numbers

Look at the timesheet.

How could you figure out the total number of hours Chang worked in this week?

Emma changed all the fractions to a common denominator. Then she added the fractions and the whole hours.

Describe the steps you think Emma used.

What total would she get?

Chang's Timesheet	
Monday	$1\frac{1}{4}$ hours
Tuesday	$1\frac{1}{2}$ hours
Wednesday	$1\frac{3}{4}$ hours
Thursday	$\frac{3}{4}$ hour
Friday	$1\frac{1}{2}$ hours

Cole added pairs of times that made whole hours first. Then he added the times that were left.

He recorded his thinking like this.

$$1\frac{1}{4} + 1\frac{3}{4} = 3$$

$$1\frac{1}{2} + 1\frac{1}{2} = 3$$

$$3 + 3 + \frac{3}{4} = 6\frac{3}{4}$$

Describe the steps Cole followed.

What is another way you could add the times?

Step Up

1. Solve each problem. Show your thinking. You can draw a picture to help.

a. Mrs. Waters bought 3 lengths of fabric that measured $2\frac{1}{2}$ yd, $3\frac{2}{3}$ yd, and $1\frac{1}{4}$ yd. How many yards of fabric did she buy in total?

_____ yd

b. Mr. Reed bought a strip of wood to make a picture frame that measured $3\frac{3}{4}$ ft by $1\frac{1}{2}$ ft. What was the total length of the strip of wood he bought?

_____ ft

2. Solve these problems. Show your thinking.

a. The cleaners worked $7\frac{3}{4}$ hours on Tuesday and $6\frac{1}{3}$ hours on Wednesday to clean a large building. How much time did they take to clean the building?

_____ hr

b. A school needs rope to place around a new triangular-shaped garden. Two sides of the triangle are $8\frac{3}{4}$ yd long. The third side is $6\frac{2}{3}$ yd long. What length of rope is needed?

_____ yd

c. Three bags of fruit weighed $3\frac{3}{8}$ lb, $2\frac{3}{4}$ lb, and $2\frac{1}{2}$ lb. What was the total weight of all the fruit?

_____ lb

Step Ahead

Time in hours can be written as common fractions or as decimal fractions. For example, $2\frac{1}{4}$ hours could be written as 2.25 hours.

Rewrite Chang's timesheet as decimal fractions. Then add to find the total hours he worked.

Monday $1\frac{1}{4}$ hours = _____ . _____ hours   Tuesday $1\frac{1}{2}$ hours = _____ . _____ hours

Wednesday $1\frac{3}{4}$ hours = _____ . _____ hours   Thursday $\frac{3}{4}$ hour = _____ . _____ hour

Friday $1\frac{1}{2}$ hours = _____ . _____ hours

Total is _____ hours.

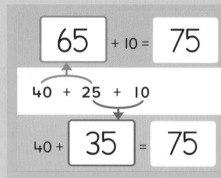

When I add three numbers, I can work in any order.

But I don't get the same answer when I subtract in different orders.

65 + 10 = 75		15 – 10 = 5
40 + 25 + 10		40 – 25 – 10
40 + 35 = 75		40 – 15 = 25

What do you think will happen when you multiply or divide in different orders?

80 × 2 = ____		____ ÷ 2 = ____
20 × 4 × 2		20 ÷ 4 ÷ 2
20 × 8 = ____		20 ÷ ____ = ____

What do you notice? Which operations can you work with in different orders?

Step Up

1. Add to figure out the missing numbers. Write the totals.

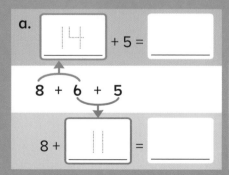

a.
14 + 5 = ____

8 + 6 + 5

8 + 11 = ____

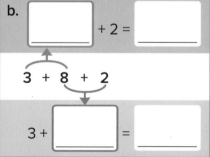

b.
____ + 2 = ____

3 + 8 + 2

3 + ____ = ____

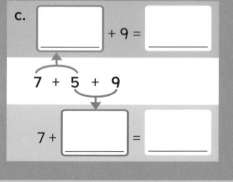

c.
____ + 9 = ____

7 + 5 + 9

7 + ____ = ____

2. Write the missing numbers. Then write the answers.

a. 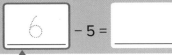 [6] − 5 = _____

13 − 7 − 5

13 − [2] = _____

b. [ ] − 5 = _____

18 − 9 − 5

18 − [ ] = _____

c. [ ] − 3 = _____

15 − 11 − 3

15 − [ ] = _____

d. [ ] × 2 = _____

3 × 5 × 2

3 × [ ] = _____

e. [ ] × 3 = _____

4 × 2 × 3

4 × [ ] = _____

f. [ ] × 6 = _____

2 × 5 × 6

2 × [ ] = _____

g. [ ] ÷ 2 = _____

24 ÷ 6 ÷ 2

24 ÷ [ ] = _____

h. [ ] ÷ 2 = _____

40 ÷ 10 ÷ 2

40 ÷ [ ] = _____

i. [ ] ÷ 3 = _____

36 ÷ 6 ÷ 3

36 ÷ [ ] = _____

3. Look at your answers in Questions 1 and 2. Write what you notice.

_____

_____

_____

Step Ahead Write numbers to make true equations. You can use a calculator to help.

[ ] + [ ] + [ ] = 64

[ ] × [ ] × [ ] = 64

[ ] − [ ] − [ ] = 64

[ ] ÷ [ ] ÷ [ ] = 64

How could you figure out the number of cubes in this prism?

This prism is 4 layers high. Each layer has 6 rows and 3 cubes in each row. So I would multiply 4 x 6 x 3.

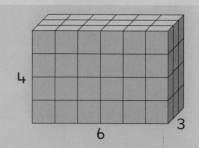

What would you write to show your thinking?

Which part is easier to multiply? Why?

How many cubes are in the prism?

You don't need parentheses for multiplication but they do tell which two factors to multiply first.

Here is another example where parentheses are used to help.

How would you figure out the total number of squares in this array?

5

23

The rows can be split into parts to make it easier to figure out. How have these rows been split?

5

20 + 3

Look at these equations. What do you notice?

$5 \times 23 = 5 \times (20 + 3)$

$5 \times (20 + 3) = (5 \times 20) + (5 \times 3)$

Step Up

1. Write an equation with parentheses to show how to figure out the total number of cubes in each prism. Make sure you write the total.

a.

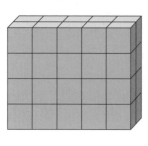

_____

b.

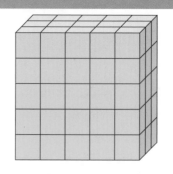

_____

2. For each equation, write the product. Then  loop the part that shows how you multiplied.

a.

$(7 × 4) × 5 = \underline{} = 7 × (4 × 5)$

b.

$(2 × 8) × 6 = \underline{} = 2 × (8 × 6)$

c.

$(3 × 4) × 5 = \underline{} = 3 × (4 × 5)$

d.

$(9 × 2) × 5 = \underline{} = 9 × (2 × 5)$

3. Color each rectangle to show how you could split it into two parts to figure out the area.
Complete each equation.

a.

24

5

$5 × (\underline{} + \underline{}) = 5 × \underline{} + 5 × \underline{}$

b.
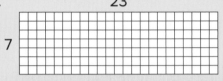
23

7

$7 × (\underline{} + \underline{}) = \underline{} × \underline{} + \underline{} × \underline{}$

4. Kylie and Ashley figured out two expressions in different ways.
Complete the expressions to show how they thought. Then write the product.

a. 4 × 28

Kylie $4 × (20 + 8) = 4 × \underline{} + 4 × \underline{}$

Ashley $4 × (25 + 3) = 4 × \underline{} + 4 × \underline{}$

$4 × 28 = \underline{}$

b. 3 × 36

Kylie $3 × (30 + 6) = 3 × \underline{} + 3 × \underline{}$

Ashley $3 × (33 + 3) = 3 × \underline{} + 3 × \underline{}$

$3 × 36 = \underline{}$

Step Ahead

8 × 49

a. Read the expression.
Complete both equations.

$8 × (40 + 9) = 8 × \underline{} + \underline{} × \underline{} = \underline{}$

$8 × (50 − 1) = 8 × \underline{} − \underline{} × \underline{} = \underline{}$

b. What do you notice about the products for the two equations? Which operations are used?

_____

_____

Look at these word problems.

> Ramon bought a new shirt for $39, shorts for $19, and shoes for $75. What was the total cost?

> Teena bought 3 boxes of muffins. In each box, there were 4 flavors with 6 muffins in each flavor. How many muffins did she buy?

What expression could you write to solve each problem?

Why are parentheses not needed?

What steps would you use to figure out each answer?

> An **expression** is a combination of numbers and operations that do not show a relationship, for example, 5 × 8 or 40 + 3.

Look at these word problems.
Write one expression for each to show how you would figure out the answer.

> Grace bought a cap for $18 and 4 pairs of socks for $9 a pair. What was the total cost?

> One box of muffins is $12. Peter used $50 to pay for 3 boxes of muffins. How much change should he get back?

Why are parentheses not needed for these expressions?

What steps would you use to figure out each answer?

> Remember, without parentheses, multiplication and division are always done before addition or subtraction.

Step Up ▶ 1. Write an expression to show how to solve the problem. You do not need to figure out the answer.

a. Tia has already saved $85. She plans to save $6 each week for the next 5 weeks. How much will she have saved after 5 weeks?

b. Amos needs 6 strips of ribbon. Each strip is 5 ft long. The ribbon costs $2 a foot. What is the total cost of the ribbon he needs?

2. Write an expression to show how to solve each problem. You do not need to figure out the answer.

a. A road rally began at 8 a.m. The first car finished the race in $2\frac{1}{2}$ hours. The last car crossed the finish line $\frac{3}{4}$ of an hour later. What time did the last car finish the race?

b. Isabelle gave $15 to each of the five children. David also gave the children $60 to share equally. How much money was each child given?

c. Small bottles of water are 55 cents each. Large bottles are 95 cents each. How much more do 6 small bottles cost than 3 large bottles?

d. Caps are $3 each and visors are $2 each. What is the total cost of 6 caps and 4 visors?

3. Loop the part that you would do first in each of these expressions.

a.	**b.**	**c.**	**d.**
$75 + 5 \times 12$	$75 \times 5 - 12$	$75 - 5 \times 12$	$75 \div 5 - 12$

e.	**f.**	**g.**	**h.**
$75 \times 5 \times 12$	$75 \times 5 + 12$	$75 + 5 - 12$	$75 \div 5 + 12$

Step Ahead Write a word problem that matches each expression.

a. $75 + 5 - 12$

b. $75 \times 5 + 12$

Look at these word problems.

> A school used 4 buses for a trip to a football game. Each bus carried 25 students and 10 adults. How many passengers were on all 4 buses?

> Trina had $50. She bought a $35 game. At the checkout, $5 was taken off the price of the game. How much did she have left after she paid for the game?

Write an expression you could use to solve each problem. Why are parentheses needed in each expression?

If you changed these expressions to equations, what steps could you use to figure out each answer?

Could you rewrite the expressions without parentheses and still get the correct answer? How?

Look at these word problems.

> Six students bought food for $28 and drinks for $11. They shared the cost equally. How much did each student pay?

> Victor earns $85 each week and spends $68 each week. He saves what is left over. How much will he save in 12 weeks?

Write an expression that uses parentheses to show how you could figure out each answer.

If you changed these expressions to equations, what steps could you use to figure out each answer?

Step Up ▶ 1. Color the ⬭ beside the expression that matches the steps you would use to figure out the answer to the problem.

a. Each book costs $8 plus 50 cents for tax. How much will you pay for 6 books?

○ 6 × (8 + 0.50)   ○ 8 + 0.50 × 6
○ 6 × 8 + 0.50   ○ (6 × 8) + 0.50

b. 12 adults and 23 children were split into 5 equal teams. How many people were on each team?

○ 12 + 23 ÷ 5   ○ (12 + 23) ÷ 5
○ 12 + (23 ÷ 5)   ○ 12 ÷ 5 + 23

c. Julia had $35 and bought an $18 game. Then her gran gave her $5. How much does she have now?

○ 35 − (18 + 5)   ○ 35 − (18 − 5)
○ (35 − 18) + 5   ○ 35 + (5 − 18)

d. The perimeter of a rectangle is 22 feet. The two long sides total 14 feet. What is the width of the rectangle?

○ 22 − 14 ÷ 2   ○ 22 − (14 ÷ 2)
○ (22 − 14) ÷ 2   ○ (22 ÷ 2) − 14

2. For each problem, write an expression to show how you would figure out the answer. You do not need to write the answer.

a. Large bottles of water that normally cost $2.50 have been reduced by 60 cents. What is the total cost of 5 large bottles of water?

b. Peta and Evan each gave $38 to their 4 children to share equally. How much money will each child get?

c. Jie runs 4 miles every morning and 7 miles every evening. How far does he run in 5 days?

d. Alisa went shopping with $75. She bought a $29 gift and then spent $15 on lunch. How much money does she have left?

3. In each equation, draw parentheses if they are needed to make it true.

a. $5 \times 0 + 20 = 100$

b. $26 + 47 + 5 = 78$

c. $24 \div 4 \times 2 = 3$

d. $38 - 21 + 38 = 55$

e. $12 - 8 \times 4 = 16$

f. $2 \times 32 \div 4 = 16$

g. $3 + 7 \times 4 \div 2 = 20$

h. $100 = 31 + 9 \times 2 + 20$

i. $55 \div 5 - 6 + 1 = 4$

Step Ahead   Write a word problem to match this expression. $8 \times (4 + 5)$

5.1   Comparing and Ordering Thousandths

How do you say each of these decimal fractions?

| 0 | . | 5 | 3 | 0 | | 0 | . | 7 | 0 | 5 |

How could you compare the two decimal fractions to figure out which is greater?

You could shade each fraction on a thousandths grid. Then compare the amounts that are shaded.

I would start with the ones and compare the digits in each place.

Estimate the position of each decimal fraction on this number line.

0   I

How did you figure out each estimate?

Which fraction is greater?

Step Up

1. Draw an arrow to show the approximate position of each number on the number line. Then write the decimal fractions in order from **least** to **greatest**.

0.455   0.325   0.895   0.810

0   I

2. Write each set of fractions in order from **least** to **greatest**. Use the number line to help you.

a.

| 0.505 | 0.890 | 0.550 | 0.915 |

0 ——————————————————————————— 1

[   ] [   ] [   ] [   ]

b.

| 0.075 | 0.210 | 0.740 | 0.501 |

0 ——————————————————————————— 1

[   ] [   ] [   ] [   ]

3. In each group, loop the **greatest** fraction.

a.

| 0.435 | 0.800 | 0.590 |

b.

| 0.605 | 0.650 | 0.065 |

c.

| 0.795 | 0.957 | 0.597 |

d.

| 0.002 | 0.020 | 0.102 |

4. Write **<** or **>** to make each statement true.

a. 0.505 ◯ 0.055

b. 0.189 ◯ 0.198

c. 0.065 ◯ 0.056

d. 0.021 ◯ 0.102

e. 0.110 ◯ 0.011

f. 0.900 ◯ 0.099

Step Ahead

Kayla records the fastest lap time of 45.275 seconds.
Gavin records a lap time that is 0.009 of a second slower.

What is Gavin's lap time? _____ seconds

Comparing and Ordering All Decimal Fractions

Where would you show this decimal fraction on the number line?

How did you figure it out? What part of the decimal fraction did you look at first?

Is this decimal fraction greater than or less than 0.52?
Where would you show 0.527 on the number line?

Is this decimal fraction greater than or less than 0.52?
How did you decide?

Which of these decimal fractions is the greatest? Which is the least? How did you decide?

I find it easiest to convert each decimal fraction to thousandths. That's 0.420, 0.406, and 0.400.

Step Up I. Draw an arrow to show the approximate position of each decimal fraction on the number line. Then write them in order from **least** to **greatest**.

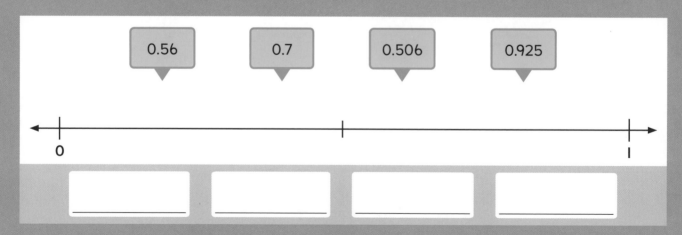

© ORIGO Education.

2. Write each set of decimal fractions in order from **least** to **greatest**.
Use the number line to help you.

a.

| 0.32 | 0.03 | 0.375 | 0.505 |

b.

| 0.786 | 0.065 | 0.7 | 0.65 |

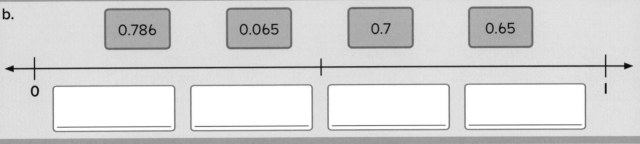

c.

| 0.51 | 0.005 | 0.79 | 0.703 |

3. Write these in order from **greatest** to **least**.

| 0.5 | 0.425 | 0.475 | 0.45 | 0.54 | 0.505 |

_____ _____ _____ _____ _____ _____

4. Write **<**, **>**, or **=** to make each statement true.

a. 0.5 ◯ 0.425

b. 0.099 ◯ 0.02

c. 0.06 ◯ 0.016

d. 0.109 ◯ 0.19

e. 0.2 ◯ 0.200

f. 0.411 ◯ 0.46

Step Ahead ▶ Write six decimal fractions that are greater than 0.497 but less than 0.51.

On this number line, the distance between each whole number is one whole. Where would you show this decimal fraction on the number line?

1.391

What is the nearest whole number? How do you know?

Mark the same decimal fraction on this number line. Be as accurate as possible.

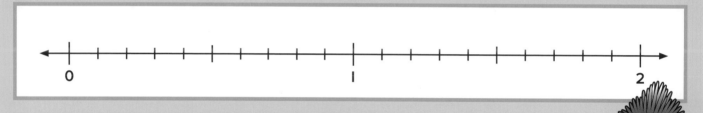

What is the nearest tenth? How do you know?

1.391 is very close to 1.4.

The number line below shows thousandths. What numbers are between 1.39 and 1.40?

What hundredth is nearest to 1.391? How did you decide?

Step Up

1. Draw an arrow to show the approximate position of each number on the number line. Then write the nearest **whole number**.

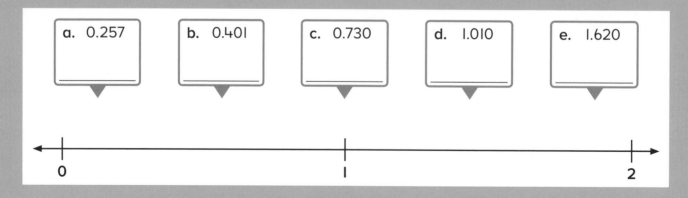

a. 0.257   b. 0.401   c. 0.730   d. 1.010   e. 1.620

2. Draw an arrow to show the approximate position of each number on the number line. Then write the nearest **tenth**.

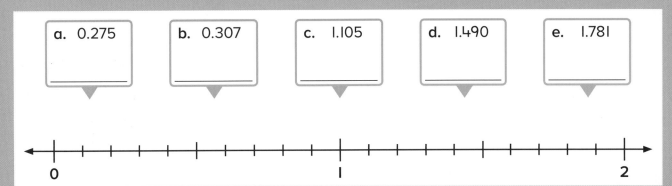

| a. 0.275 | b. 0.307 | c. 1.105 | d. 1.490 | e. 1.781 |

3. Draw an arrow to show the exact position of each number on the number line. Then write the nearest **hundredth**.

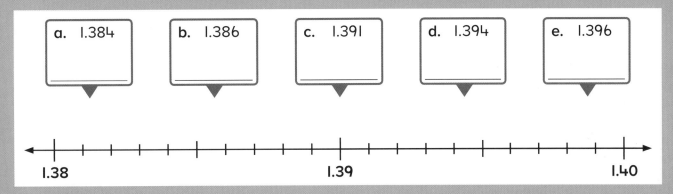

| a. 1.384 | b. 1.386 | c. 1.391 | d. 1.394 | e. 1.396 |

4. Read the number on the expander. Then round each number to the nearest whole number, tenth, and hundredth.

	Nearest whole number	Nearest tenth	Nearest hundredth
a. 3. 8 7 2			
b. 5. 2 1 9			

Step Ahead Explain how you would round this number to the nearest **tenth**.

6. 4 9 2

5.4 ▶ Rounding All Decimal Fractions

Franco's arm span measures 1.417 m and Layla's arm span measures 1.471 m.

How could you round each length to shorten the decimal fractions?

Should you round to the nearest whole number or to the nearest tenth? Why?

Which whole meters are each arm span between?

Which whole meter is each arm span nearest?

Which tenths of a meter are each arm span between?

Which tenth of a meter is each arm span nearest?

Mark and label each length on this number line.

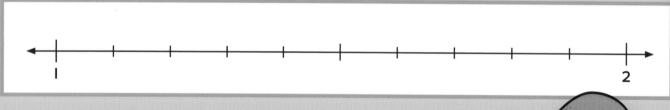

How do you know which tenth is closer?

What helped you decide?

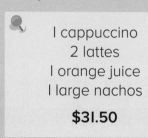

Step Up

1. Use a calculator to figure out these even shares.
   Then round each share to the nearest tenth.

a. This order was shared by four friends.

🔍 1 cappuccino
2 lattes
1 orange juice
1 large nachos

$31.50

$ _____ each

b. This order was shared by three friends.

🔍 3 bottled water
3 muffins
1 pizza

$36.50

$ _____ each

c. This order was shared by four friends.

🔍 1 fried rice
1 beef chow mein
4 spring rolls
2 prawn toast

$47.90

$ _____ each

2. For each number, draw an arrow to show its approximate position on the number line. Then write the whole number that is closest.

| a. 0.62 | b. 0.26 | c. 2.001 | d. 2.9 | e. 3.25 | f. 3.45 |

```
<--+-------+-------+-------+-------+-->
   0       1       2       3       4
```

| g. 8.450 | h. 8.9 | i. 9.85 | j. 10.15 | k. 11.05 | l. 11.990 |

```
<--+-------+-------+-------+-------+-->
   8       9      10      11      12
```

3. For each number, draw an arrow to show its approximate position on the number line. Then round each number to the nearest tenth.

| a. 0.15 | b. 0.402 | c. 0.940 | d. 1.23 | e. 1.57 | f. 1.835 |

```
<--+-+-+-+-+-+-+-+-+-+-+-+-+-+-+-+-+-+-+-+-->
   0                   1                   2
```

Step Ahead

a. Loop the decimal fractions that you would round to 1.3.

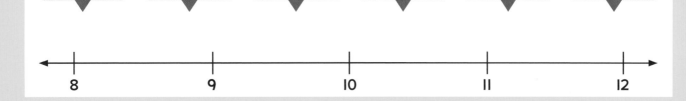

| 1.247 | 1.209 | 1.31 | 1.268 | 1.375 | 1.03 |

b. How did you decide?

_____

_____

© ORIGO Education.

Adding Decimal Fractions

This table shows the amount of protein in some fast foods.

How could you figure out the total protein
for one lean burger and one serving of fries?

Zola added the ones first, then the tenths.

Big Burger Bar

Lean Burger	15.3 g
Fries	3.4 g
Onion Rings	5.12 g
Potato Skins	1.65 g

Jack used a number line to figure out the total.

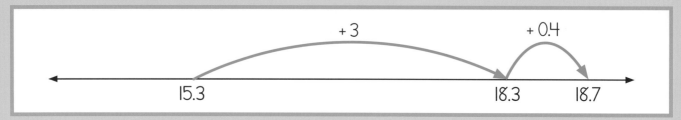

What steps did he follow? How is Jack's strategy different from Zola's strategy?

What are some other totals that you can figure out?

Luis figured out the total protein for one serving of fries and one serving of onion rings.

He showed his thinking on this number line.

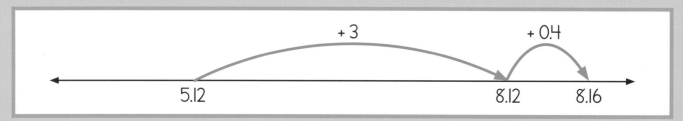

What did he do wrong?

Step Up   I.   Draw jumps on the number line to figure out each total.

a.

2.3 + 5.4 = ☐

b.

4.5 + 3.1 = ☐

2. Figure out each total. Draw jumps to show your thinking.

a.

$6.2 + 1.37 =$ _____

b.

$2.05 + 5.6 =$ _____

3. Figure out the total cost. Show your thinking.

a.

$2.40 $1.30

$ _____

b.

$6.05 $2.50

$ _____

c.

$3.25 $4.31

$ _____

d.

$7.13 $1.82

$ _____

Step Ahead   Write the value of each coin as a decimal fraction of one dollar.

_____   _____   _____   _____

Adding Decimal Fractions (with Regrouping)

These students threw a shot put twice and added the distances.

	1st Throw	2nd Throw	Total
Andre	3.5 m	3.7 m	m
Lilly	3.09 m	3.45 m	m
Jacob	4.2 m	3.92 m	m

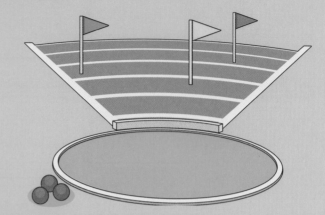

How could you figure out the total distance of Andre's throws?

How could you figure out the total distance of Lilly's throws?

 Carlos figured out the total like this.

3.09 + 3.45

3 + 3 = 6

0.0 + 0.4 = 0.4

0.09 + 0.05 = 0.14

6.54

 Amber figured it out like this.

3.09 + 3.45

$3\frac{9}{100} + 3\frac{45}{100} = 6\frac{54}{100}$

Mary figured out 3.10 + 3.44.
She knew it would give the same total.

What steps does each person follow? Which strategy do you prefer? Why?

Use the strategy you like best to figure out the total length of Jacob's throws.

Who threw the greatest total distance?

Step Up

1. Figure out each total. Show your thinking.

a.
3.6 + 4.8 = _____

b.
2.65 + 3.18 = _____

c.
5.71 + 2.63 = _____

2. Figure out each total. Show your thinking.

a.

$3.80 $4.30

$ _____

b.

$1.90 $5.60

$ _____

c.

$2.38 $2.45

$ _____

d.

$7.62 $1.09

$ _____

e.

$5.40 $1.70

$ _____

f.

$3.85 $2.90

$ _____

Step Ahead Figure out and write the missing lengths.

	1st Throw	2nd Throw	Total
Megan	3.5 m	m	7.02 m
Carmen	m	4.25 m	9.2 m
James	m	m	8.05 m

3.50 + ? = 7.02

These two packages were weighed in kilograms.

Estimate the mass of the two packages together.

5.72 kg

6.8 kg

How could you figure out the exact mass of the two packages?

These numbers are too messy to add in my head. I need to write them down.

Cody used the standard addition algorithm to figure out the total. What steps did he follow?

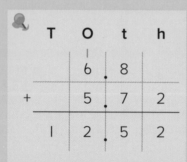

T	O	t	h
	1		
	6 .	8	
+	5 .	7	2
1	2 .	5	2

Step Up > 1. Calculate the total mass of each pair of packages.

a.

8.34 kg

3.25 kg

T	O	t	h
	8 .	3	4
+	3 .	2	5

b.

12.47 kg

14.08 kg

T	O	t	h
1	2 .	4	7
+ 1	4 .	0	8

c.

6.5 kg

12.81 kg

T	O	t	h
1	2 .	8	1
+	6 .	5	

2. Calculate the total mass of these packages.

a.

6.48 kg   2.37 kg

	T	O	t	h
+				

b.

8.92 kg   5.42 kg

	T	O	t	h
+				

c.

4.73 kg   10.8 kg

	T	O	t	h
+				

d.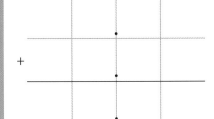

8.05 kg   7.58 kg

	T	O	t	h
+				

e.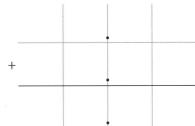

13.9 kg   7.03 kg

	T	O	t	h
+				

f.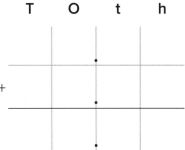

15.82 kg   6.59 kg

	T	O	t	h
+				

Step Ahead

This student seems to repeat the same error on a test.
Describe the mistake in words.

```
    2 . 3
+   4 . 6
    6 . 9
```

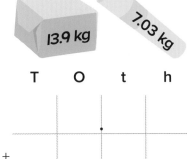

```
    4 . 7
+   3 . 8
    7 . 15
```

```
    5 . 2
+   3 . 5
    8 . 7
```

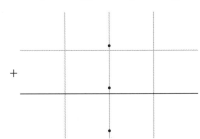

```
    7 . 3
+   7 . 9
   14 . 12
```

_____
_____
_____
_____

Using a Written Method to Add More Than Two Decimal Fractions

Estimate the perimeter of this triangle.

Each side is just over one meter, so the perimeter is between 3 and 4 meters.

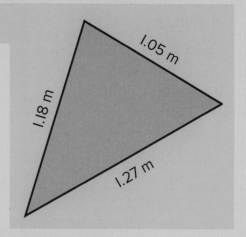

1.05 m

1.18 m

1.27 m

How could you figure out the exact perimeter?

Liam and Sumi both used a written method.

Liam added the hundredths first.

$$\begin{array}{r} \overset{2}{} \\ 1.18 \\ 1.27 \\ +\ 1.05 \\ \hline 3.50 \end{array}$$

Sumi added the ones first.

$$\begin{array}{r} 1.18 \\ 1.27 \\ +\ 1.05 \\ \hline 3.00 \\ 0.30 \\ 0.20 \\ \hline 3.50 \end{array}$$

Is there another way you could do it?

Step Up ▶   **I.** Use a written method to calculate the perimeter of each triangle. Record the steps you use.

a.

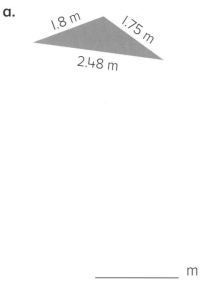

1.8 m   1.75 m

2.48 m

_____ m

b.

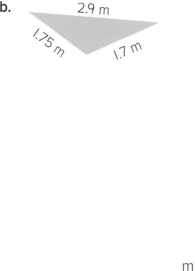

2.9 m

1.75 m   1.7 m

_____ m

c.

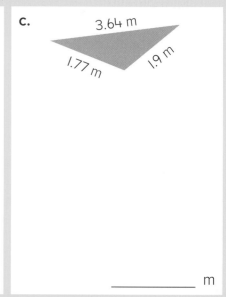

3.64 m

1.77 m   1.9 m

_____ m

2. Calculate these perimeters. Record the steps you use.

a.
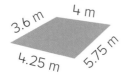

_____ m

b.

_____ m

c.

_____ m

d.
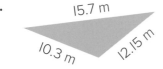

_____ m

e.
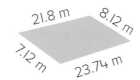

_____ m

f.
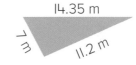

_____ m

Step Ahead

Draw and label a shape that has sides
of different length and a perimeter of
10 meters. Show each side measure as
a decimal fraction involving hundredths.

5.9 ▸ Describing Polygons

 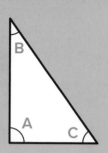

Make a triangle by cutting a sheet of paper in half like this. Then label each corner as shown.

What types of angles are the corners?

What type of angle do you think each of these combinations will make?

A + C will make an _____ angle.

B + C will make a _____ angle.

A + B will make an _____ angle.

These shapes have been made with two or more of the triangles.

Shape R	Shape S	Shape T	Shape U
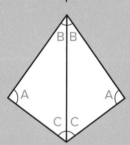	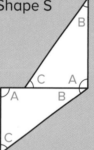		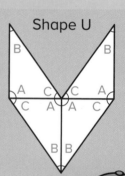

Shape R is a quadrilateral. It has two short sides and two long sides. It also has two right angles, one acute angle, and one obtuse angle.

How would you describe the other shapes?

Step Up ▸ Describe each whole shape. Be as accurate as you can.

a.

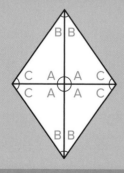

_____

_____

_____

_____

120

ORIGO Stepping Stones 5 • 5.9

© ORIGO Education.

b.

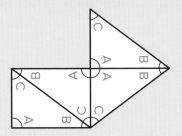

_____

_____

_____

_____

c.

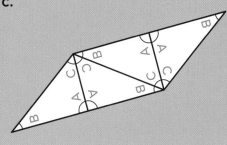

_____

_____

_____

_____

d.

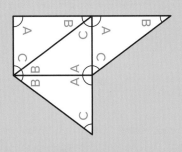

_____

_____

_____

_____

Step Ahead Use 2, 3, or 4 triangles to make two different quadrilaterals.
Draw each shape you make.

a.

b.

5.10 ▶ Identifying Parallelograms

Think about the quadrilaterals you know.

What do you know about the angles of rectangles?

What do you know about the sides of rhombuses?

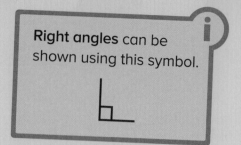

Right angles can be shown using this symbol.

A square is a type of rectangle and also a type of rhombus. Why?

Parallelograms are quadrilaterals that have two pairs of parallel sides.

What are all the ways of describing each shape below?

What do you think the arrows mean?

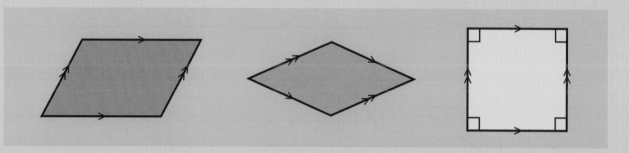

Step Up ▶ Cut out the shapes from the support page.

a. Paste the parallelograms in the space below.

b. Paste the shapes that are not parallelograms in the space below.

c. Look at the parallelograms you pasted on page 122.

Which shapes are also rectangles? _____

Step Ahead   Draw these shapes.

a.

Another example of a parallelogram

b.

A quadrilateral that is not a parallelogram

What do you know about the shapes in this tree diagram?

Draw a shape to match the label for each white box.
Look at the shapes you sorted on pages 122 and 123 to help you.

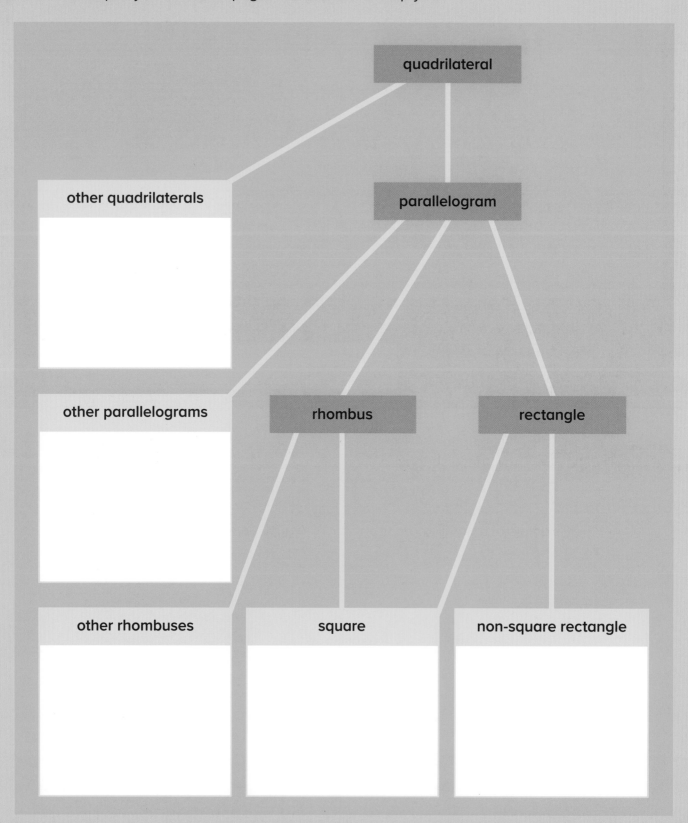

I. Write **P** inside the parallelograms.

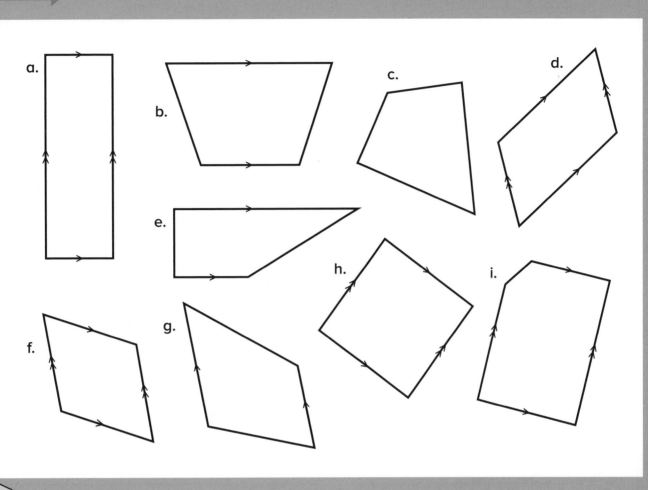

2. ⟨Loop⟩ two parallelograms above. Write three things they have in common.

_____

_____

_____

Step Ahead

Choose one parallelogram and one of the other shapes from Question I. Write how they are the same and how they are different.

_____

_____

_____

Identifying Categories of Triangles

Measure the sides of these triangles.

Why do you think these are called **equilateral triangles**?

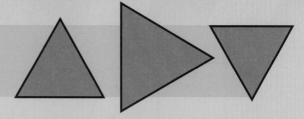

These shapes are called **isosceles triangles**.
How are they all the same?

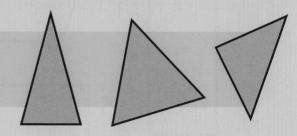

These shapes are called **scalene triangles**.
How are these different from the other triangles?

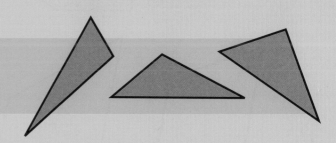

Step Up

I. For each triangle below, use the same color to mark the sides that are the same length.

2. Draw and label three equilateral triangles, three isosceles triangles, and three scalene triangles. Make each triangle different.

Step Ahead

a. Use a centimeter ruler to draw two angle arms that are each 8 cm long. Draw a third line to create a triangle.

b. What type of triangle did you make? _____

Subtracting Common Fractions and Mixed Numbers (Same Denominators)

Each hexagon is one whole.

Use red, blue, or green pattern blocks to explain how you could figure out the unknown value below.

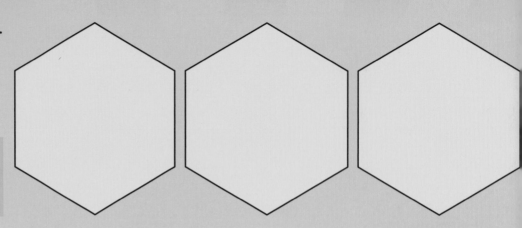

$2\frac{1}{3} - 1\frac{2}{3} = \boxed{}$

How could you figure out the unknown value by starting with $2\frac{1}{3}$?

> I would start with $2\frac{1}{3}$ and count back 1 then $\frac{2}{3}$.

How could you figure out the unknown value by starting with $1\frac{2}{3}$?

> I would count on to $2\frac{1}{3}$. The amount I count on would be the difference.

How could you use improper fractions to figure out the unknown value?

> I would change both mixed numbers to improper fractions. That's $\frac{7}{3} - \frac{5}{3}$.

Which strategy could you use to figure out the difference in each of these equations?

$3 - 1\frac{1}{6} = \boxed{}$

$3 - \frac{5}{3} = \boxed{}$

Step Up

1. Complete each equation. Rewrite fractions or mixed numbers if necessary to help you figure out the unknown difference.

a.

$\frac{15}{6} - \frac{7}{6} = \boxed{}$

b.

$\frac{7}{3} - \frac{4}{3} = \boxed{}$

c.

$2\frac{5}{6} - 1\frac{1}{6} = \boxed{}$

d.

$1\frac{2}{3} - 1\frac{1}{3} = \boxed{}$

2. Figure out the unknown value in each equation. Rewrite one or both numbers to help.

a.

$2\frac{1}{6} - \frac{11}{6} =$ ☐

b.

$\frac{10}{3} - 1\frac{1}{3} =$ ☐

3. Complete each equation. Use the number line to help rewrite one or both numbers.

a.

$2\frac{3}{4} - \frac{5}{4} =$ ☐

b.

$\frac{17}{8} - 1\frac{5}{8} =$ ☐

c.

$2\frac{1}{4} - 1\frac{3}{4} =$ ☐

d.

$2\frac{1}{8} - 1\frac{3}{8} =$ ☐

Step Ahead ▶ Complete these equations in two different ways. Use pattern blocks with the hexagon outlines at the top of page 128 to help you. The denominators must be the same.

a.

$2\frac{1}{6} -$ ☐ $=$ ☐

$2\frac{1}{6} -$ ☐ $=$ ☐

b.

☐ $- \frac{4}{3} =$ ☐

☐ $- \frac{4}{3} =$ ☐

c.

☐ $-$ ☐ $= \frac{5}{6}$

☐ $-$ ☐ $= \frac{5}{6}$

Subtracting Common Fractions (Related Denominators)

These pizzas were left over after a party.

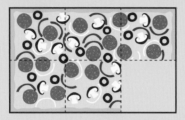

Super Supreme

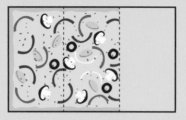

Very Veggie

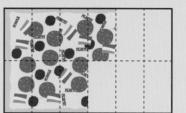

Mostly Meat

Which pizza had the most left over? How do you know?

What are some subtraction stories you could make up about the pizza?

What number sentences could you write for the stories?

What do you notice about the denominators in each pair of fractions below?

$$\frac{2}{3} - \frac{7}{12} = \frac{\quad}{\quad}$$

$$\frac{5}{6} - \frac{2}{3} = \frac{\quad}{\quad}$$

$$\frac{5}{12} - \frac{1}{3} = \frac{\quad}{\quad}$$

How could you figure out each difference? Use the space below each sentence to show your thinking.

Step Up

I. Rewrite the fractions so the denominators are the same. Use the number line to help. Complete each equation.

a.
$$\frac{4}{5} - \frac{7}{10} = \frac{\quad}{\quad}$$

b.
$$\frac{7}{20} - \frac{1}{5} = \frac{\quad}{\quad}$$

c.
$$\frac{7}{10} - \frac{7}{20} = \frac{\quad}{\quad}$$

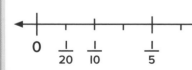

© ORIGO Education.

2. Rewrite the fractions so the denominators are the same. Complete each equation.

a.

$\dfrac{2}{3} - \dfrac{5}{9} = \boxed{\dfrac{\quad}{\quad}}$

b.

$\dfrac{5}{8} - \dfrac{7}{16} = \boxed{\dfrac{\quad}{\quad}}$

c.

$\dfrac{11}{15} - \dfrac{2}{5} = \boxed{\dfrac{\quad}{\quad}}$

d.

$\dfrac{15}{16} - \dfrac{3}{4} = \boxed{\dfrac{\quad}{\quad}}$

e.

$\dfrac{5}{20} - \dfrac{1}{4} = \boxed{\dfrac{\quad}{\quad}}$

f.

$\dfrac{19}{24} - \dfrac{2}{3} = \boxed{\dfrac{\quad}{\quad}}$

3. Find the difference in value between the two fractions in each pair. Show your thinking.

a. $\dfrac{7}{10}$ $\dfrac{3}{5}$

$\boxed{\dfrac{\quad}{\quad}}$

b. $\dfrac{11}{24}$ $\dfrac{2}{3}$

$\boxed{\dfrac{\quad}{\quad}}$

c. $\dfrac{17}{24}$ $\dfrac{3}{4}$

$\boxed{\dfrac{\quad}{\quad}}$

Step Ahead

Write a subtraction expression that is equal to each fraction. Use denominators that are different from the denominator of the fraction answer. The first one has been done for you.

$\dfrac{1}{2} = \boxed{\dfrac{3}{4} - \dfrac{1}{4}}$

$\dfrac{5}{6} = \boxed{}$

$\dfrac{2}{3} = \boxed{}$

$\dfrac{6}{7} = \boxed{}$

$\dfrac{3}{4} = \boxed{}$

$\dfrac{7}{8} = \boxed{}$

$\dfrac{4}{5} = \boxed{}$

$\dfrac{8}{9} = \boxed{}$

Subtracting Common Fractions (Unrelated Denominators)

Some parts of these pizzas have been eaten.

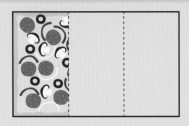

Seriously Supreme

Cheese and Cheese

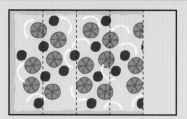

Tasty Tomato

Which pizza has the least left over? Which pizza has the most left over? How do you know?

What are some subtraction stories you could make up about the pizzas?

What equations could you write to match your stories?

What do you notice about the denominators of the fractions you wrote?

What story problem could you write to match each of these equations?

$$\frac{3}{4} - \frac{1}{3} = \boxed{}$$

$$\frac{2}{3} - \frac{1}{4} = \boxed{}$$

$$\frac{4}{5} - \frac{3}{4} = \boxed{}$$

How could you figure out each difference? Use the space below each sentence to show your thinking.

Step Up   **I.**   Find the difference between the two fractions in each pair. Show your thinking.

a. $\frac{2}{3}$ $\frac{1}{5}$

b. $\frac{1}{4}$ $\frac{1}{5}$

c. $\frac{1}{3}$ $\frac{4}{5}$

2. Rewrite **one** or **both** fractions so the denominators are the same. Complete each equation.

a.
$$\frac{1}{3} - \frac{1}{4} = \boxed{}$$

b.
$$\frac{2}{5} - \frac{1}{6} = \boxed{}$$

c.
$$\frac{3}{4} - \frac{1}{6} = \boxed{}$$

d.
$$\frac{3}{7} - \frac{1}{4} = \boxed{}$$

e.
$$\frac{5}{8} - \frac{1}{3} = \boxed{}$$

f.
$$\frac{7}{12} - \frac{3}{8} = \boxed{}$$

3. Figure out the missing value in each equation. Show your thinking.

a.
$$\frac{1}{5} = \boxed{} - \frac{1}{3}$$

b.
$$\frac{3}{8} = \boxed{} - \frac{2}{3}$$

c.
$$\boxed{} - \frac{5}{6} = \frac{3}{4}$$

Step Ahead

Look at the three pizza pictures at the top of page 132. How much more pizza is left over than has been eaten? _____

Show your thinking.

HINT

To find a common denominator, think which number is a multiple of 3, 4, **and** 5.

Jack bought these two strips of wood for a picture frame.

$5\frac{1}{4}$ feet

$7\frac{1}{2}$ feet

How could you figure out the difference in length?

Look at these students' methods.

Teena subtracted using improper fractions.	Jose subtracted the whole numbers and then subtracted the fractions.	Grace subtracted by writing one mixed number below the other.
$\frac{15}{2} - \frac{21}{4} = \boxed{}$	$7 - 5 = \boxed{}$ $\frac{1}{2} - \frac{1}{4} = \boxed{}$ $\boxed{} + \boxed{} = \boxed{}$	$\begin{array}{r} 7\frac{1}{2} \\ -\ 5\frac{1}{4} \\ \hline \end{array}$

Before they subtract, what will they need to do with the fractions?

What steps will each student follow to figure out the difference?

Step Up ➤

1. Show how you could figure out each difference in two ways. One way should use **improper fractions**. The second method should use **mixed numbers**.

a.

$3\frac{3}{4} - 1\frac{5}{8}$

Use improper fractions	Use mixed numbers

b.

$4\frac{1}{3} - 2\frac{1}{6}$

Use improper fractions	Use mixed numbers

2. Figure out each difference using improper fractions and then mixed numbers.

a.

$2\frac{7}{12} - 2\frac{1}{4}$

Use improper fractions	Use mixed numbers

b.

$3\frac{9}{10} - 2\frac{3}{5}$

Use improper fractions	Use mixed numbers

3. Look at this picture frame.

a. How much longer is the longer side than the shorter side?

$2\frac{3}{8}$ ft

_____ ft

$3\frac{1}{4}$ ft

b. If the two lengths were cut from the long strip of wood at the top of page 134, how much of the strip would be left over?

_____ ft

Step Ahead

What is the widest rectangular picture frame you could make using the two strips of wood shown at the top of page 134? Write the dimensions and show your thinking.

Length _____

Width _____

Subtracting Mixed Numbers (Unrelated Denominators)

How could you figure out the difference between the amounts of apple juice and pineapple juice in this recipe?

Fruitade

$1\frac{2}{3}$ cups apple juice

$2\frac{3}{4}$ cups pineapple juice

$2\frac{1}{3}$ cups cranberry juice

$3\frac{1}{2}$ cups soda water

Daniel changed the amounts to improper fractions to subtract.	Isabelle used mixed numbers.
$\frac{11}{4} - \frac{5}{3} = \boxed{}$	$2\frac{3}{4} - 1\frac{2}{3} = \boxed{}$

What will Daniel and Isabelle need to do before they can subtract?

How should Daniel rewrite the fractions to subtract?
What steps could he follow to figure out the difference?

How should Isabelle rewrite the fractions to subtract?
What steps could she follow to figure out the difference?

What different ways could Isabelle figure out the difference?

How could you check that Daniel's answer is the same as Isabelle's answer?

Step Up

1. Show how you could figure out each difference in two ways. One way should use **improper fractions**. The second method should use **mixed numbers**.

a. $3\frac{1}{3} - 1\frac{1}{4}$	Use improper fractions	Use mixed numbers

b. $2\frac{4}{6} - 1\frac{2}{5}$	Use improper fractions	Use mixed numbers

2. Figure out each difference using improper fractions and then mixed numbers.

a.	Use improper fractions	Use mixed numbers
$2\frac{3}{5} - 1\frac{1}{4}$		

b.	Use improper fractions	Use mixed numbers
$3\frac{3}{4} - 1\frac{1}{7}$		

3. Use the recipe at the top of page 136. Figure out the answer to each question. Show your thinking.

a. How much more soda water than cranberry juice is used for the recipe?

☐ cups

b. Trina only has $\frac{3}{4}$ cup of apple juice. How much more apple juice does she need for this recipe?

☐ cup

Step Ahead

Look at the recipe at the top of page 136.
How much more fruit juice is used in the recipe than soda water?

Show your thinking.

_____ cups

Subtracting Mixed Numbers (Unrelated Denominators and Decomposing Whole Numbers)

How could you figure out the difference between the amounts in these two pots?

Why is it necessary to rewrite the fractions?

$$3\frac{1}{3} - 1\frac{1}{2} \ = \ 3\frac{2}{6} - 1\frac{3}{6} \ = \ \boxed{}$$

Try to subtract the fractions first. What do you notice?

What could you do so you can subtract? How could you use this number line to help?

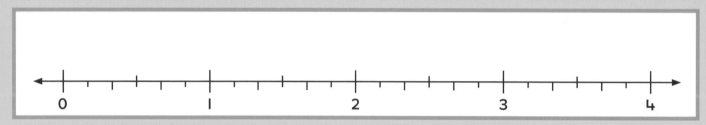

Felix wrote the mixed numbers as improper fractions first to make it easier to subtract.

$$3\frac{1}{3} - 1\frac{1}{2}$$

$$3\frac{2}{6} - 1\frac{3}{6}$$

$$\frac{\boxed{}}{6} - \frac{\boxed{}}{6} = \boxed{}$$

What steps do you think he used?
Write the missing values in his equation.

Emma worked with the mixed numbers.

$$3\frac{1}{3} - 1\frac{1}{2}$$

$$3\frac{2}{6} - 1\frac{3}{6}$$

$$2\frac{8}{6} - 1\frac{3}{6} = \boxed{}$$

What steps do you think she used?
What is the difference?

Step Up

1. For each of these, rewrite the mixed numbers so the fractions have the same denominators. Show how you subtract to find the difference.

a.	Same denominators	Show subtraction
$3\frac{1}{2} - 1\frac{2}{3}$		

b.	Same denominators	Show subtraction
$2\frac{3}{4} - 1\frac{5}{6}$		

2. Rewrite the fractions so they have the same denominators. Then subtract to figure out the difference.

a. $2\frac{1}{4} - 1\frac{1}{3}$	Same denominators	Show subtraction

b. $2\frac{2}{3} - 1\frac{3}{5}$	Same denominators	Show subtraction

3. This is another way to subtract mixed numbers. First, change both numbers to improper fractions. Then find a common denominator.

$$3\frac{1}{3} - 1\frac{1}{2} = \frac{10}{3} - \frac{3}{2} = \frac{}{6} - \frac{}{6} = \boxed{}$$

Use the same steps to figure out these differences.

a. $2\frac{1}{4} - 1\frac{3}{5}$	Change to improper fractions	Same denominators and subtract

b. $3\frac{1}{4} - 1\frac{2}{3}$	Change to improper fractions	Same denominators and subtract

c. $4\frac{1}{2} - 1\frac{3}{5}$	Change to improper fractions	Same denominators and subtract

Step Ahead

Zoe used these steps to figure out $3\frac{1}{4} - 2\frac{1}{2}$. Describe her mistake in words.

$$3 - 2 - \frac{1}{4} - \frac{1}{2}$$

Subtracting Common Fractions and Mixed Numbers (Related and Unrelated Denominators)

This game using fractions was designed by fifth grade students.
The fractions are written on the faces of two blank cubes.
Then both cubes are rolled and a subtraction sentence is written
to find the difference between the two fractions.

This table shows the scores for each pair of the denominators.

Points for denominators

- I point if one denominator must be changed to subtract.

- 2 points if both denominators must be changed to subtract.

Difference Fractions

Cube A $\frac{1}{3}$ $\frac{2}{3}$ $\frac{3}{2}$

     $\frac{1}{4}$ $\frac{3}{4}$ $\frac{4}{3}$

Cube B $\frac{1}{5}$ $\frac{4}{5}$ $\frac{6}{5}$

     $\frac{1}{6}$ $\frac{5}{6}$ $\frac{7}{6}$

What pairs of fractions could you roll using both the cubes?
What points will you score for the denominators for these rolls? Explain your thinking.

This table shows the scores for each difference.

What pairs of fractions could you roll
that will have a difference less than one?

Points for differences

- I point if the difference is less than one.

- 2 points if the difference is greater than one.

What pairs of fractions could you roll that will have a difference greater than one?

Step Up

I. Look at the ways of scoring points above. Figure out the number of points
that you would make for each of these rolls. Show your thinking.

a. $\frac{3}{2}$ $\frac{7}{6}$

Total score _____

b. $\frac{4}{3}$ $\frac{6}{5}$

Total score _____

c. $\frac{3}{4}$ $\frac{4}{5}$

Total score _____

This game is called *Difference Mixed Numbers*. It is played in the same way as the game described at the top of page 140. Points are scored for denominators and for the total.

Points for denominators	Points for totals
• I point if one denominator must be changed.	• I point if the difference is less than I.
• 2 points if both denominators must be changed.	• 2 points if the difference is greater than I.

2. Read how to score points in the game above. Then figure out the number of points that you would make for each of these rolls. Show your thinking.

a. $1\frac{1}{3}$ $2\frac{1}{2}$

Total score _____

b. $3\frac{1}{12}$ $2\frac{2}{3}$

Total score _____

c. $3\frac{2}{3}$ $2\frac{1}{5}$

Total score _____

d. $2\frac{3}{5}$ $3\frac{3}{4}$

Total score _____

Step Ahead When *Difference Fractions* is played, it is possible to score 2, 3, or 4 points.

Show two different rolls for which you could score **3 points**.

Write how you know.

How could you figure out the difference between the length and width of this garden bed?

Lara rewrote both measurements so the fractions had the same denominators.

$$4\frac{2}{6} - 2\frac{3}{6} = \boxed{}$$

Garden Bed $2\frac{1}{2}$ feet

$4\frac{1}{3}$ feet

What do you think she will do next?

How could you change both mixed numbers to improper fractions?

Jamal worked with mixed numbers but he decided to rewrite the first number. Why?

$$3\frac{8}{6} - 2\frac{3}{6} = \boxed{}$$

What is the difference between the length and the width of the garden?

Step Up

1. Solve each problem. Show your thinking. Draw a picture to help.

a. The perimeter of a garden is $13\frac{2}{3}$ yd. A roll of fencing is $15\frac{1}{2}$ yd long. How much fencing will be left over after the garden is fenced?

_____ yd

b. Peta and Jie have a length of rope that is $9\frac{1}{4}$ yd long. How much more rope do they need to stretch around a garden that has a perimeter of $13\frac{2}{3}$ yd?

_____ yd

c. Cole lives $2\frac{3}{8}$ miles from school. His friend lives $1\frac{3}{4}$ miles from school. How much farther from the school does Cole live?

_____ mi

2. Solve these problems. Show your thinking.

a. Cleaners from the Neat and Tidy Company worked $7\frac{3}{4}$ hours on Monday and $6\frac{1}{3}$ hours on Tuesday to clean a large building. How much longer did they work on Monday?

_____ hr

b. A recipe needs $3\frac{2}{3}$ cups of flour and $1\frac{1}{4}$ cups of sugar. How much more flour than sugar does the recipe use?

_____ cups

c. Two packages together weighed $14\frac{3}{8}$ lb. The heavier package weighed $9\frac{1}{2}$ lb. What was the weight of the lighter package?

_____ lb

Step Ahead David and Julia are brother and sister.

Julia said she was $1\frac{1}{2}$ yd tall and her brother was $2\frac{1}{4}$ yd tall.

David said he was $6\frac{3}{4}$ ft tall and his sister was $4\frac{1}{2}$ ft tall.

Use each person's measurements to find the difference in their heights. Show your thinking.

Difference using Julia's measurements is _____ yd.

Difference using David's measurements is _____ ft.

6.9 Converting Between Inches and Feet

This picture shows flood levels over three years.

What do you know about each level?

How would you say each of these in inches?

> I would convert the feet to inches.
> I know there are 12 inches in 1 ft.

How could you figure out the number of inches in half a foot?

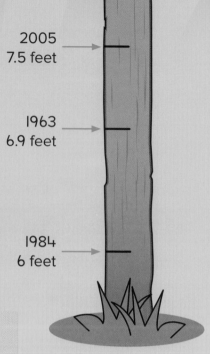

2005
7.5 feet

1963
6.9 feet

1984
6 feet

Complete these statements.

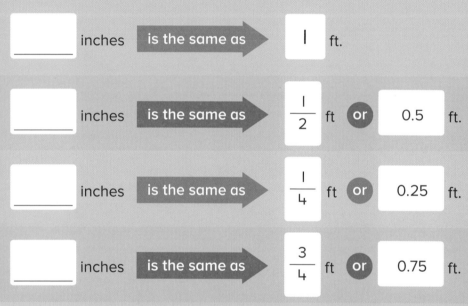

| _____ inches | is the same as | 1 ft. |

| _____ inches | is the same as | $\frac{1}{2}$ ft **or** 0.5 ft. |

| _____ inches | is the same as | $\frac{1}{4}$ ft **or** 0.25 ft. |

| _____ inches | is the same as | $\frac{3}{4}$ ft **or** 0.75 ft. |

> It's difficult to convert decimal fractions like 0.9 feet into inches.

Step Up

1. Convert inches into feet to complete these.

a. 14 inches = _____ ft _____ in

b. 28 inches = _____ ft _____ in

c. 20 inches = _____ ft _____ in

d. 33 inches = _____ ft _____ in

e. 48 inches = _____ ft _____ in

f. 39 inches = _____ ft _____ in

2. Convert feet to inches to complete these. Show your thinking.

a.
4.5 ft = [____] in

b.
3.25 ft = [____] in

c.
6.5 ft = [____] in

d.
5.75 ft = [____] in

e.
$7\frac{1}{2}$ ft = [____] in

f.
$8\frac{3}{4}$ ft = [____] in

3. Solve each problem. Show your thinking.

a. 15 inches of rain is recorded in July. This is 4 inches more than the month before. What is the total rainfall for June and July?

_____ feet _____ inches

b. This year's record flood is 8 inches higher than the previous record of 7.5 feet. What is the height of this year's flood?

_____ feet _____ inches

Step Ahead

The record flood level in Brady's town is 8.5 ft. The 2008 flood was 9 inches lower. Write the height of the 2008 flood beside the tide mark.

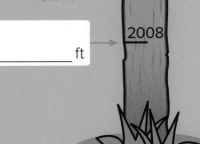

8.5 ft → 2012

→ 2008
_____ ft

Two friends play a game of golf. At the first hole, Carter's ball stops 4 yards from the hole. Emily's ball stops 15 feet from the hole.

Whose ball is closer to the hole? How do you know?

> I know there are 3 feet in 1 yard.

Carter misses his first putt.

His ball is now $2\frac{1}{3}$ yards from the hole.

How could you say this distance in feet?

> You could write the equation Y = F x 3 to describe the relationship between feet and yards.

What does the equation mean?

How could you use division to show the relationship?

Step Up

1. Convert yards to feet to complete these.

a.
6 yd = _____ ft

b.
15 yd = _____ ft

c.
9 yd = _____ ft

d.
$5\frac{1}{3}$ yd = _____ ft

e.
18 yd = _____ ft

f.
$8\frac{1}{2}$ yd = _____ ft

2. Convert feet to yards to complete these.

a.
_____ yd = 18 ft

b.
_____ yd = 42 ft

c.
_____ yd = 33 ft

d.
_____ yd = 48 ft

e.
_____ yd = 75 ft

f.
_____ yd = 63 ft

2. Solve each problem. Show your thinking.

a. At the second hole, Carter's ball stops $7\frac{2}{3}$ yards from the hole. Emily's ball stops 16 feet from the hole. How much closer is Emily's ball to the hole?

_____ feet

b. At the sixth hole, Carter hits the ball 120 yd on his first shot, which is 9 feet farther than Emily. What was the length of Emily's first shot?

_____ yards

c. The fifth hole is 186 yards in length. Carter's first shot stops 12 feet from the hole. What is the length of his first shot?

_____ yards

d. The 7th hole is 75 feet shorter than the 9th hole. The 9th hole is 317 yd long. What is the length of the 7th hole?

_____ yards

Step Ahead

The 18th hole is 324 yards long. Carter's first shot stops 135 yards from the hole. His second shot stops 9 feet from the hole.

What was the length of each shot?   1st shot _____ yd   2nd shot _____ yd

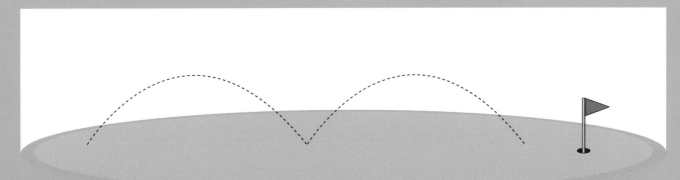

6.11 Converting Between Inches, Feet, Yards, and Miles

What do you know about the distances on this sign?

How many yards are in one mile?

How could you figure out the number of yards
in half a mile? ... in quarter of a mile?

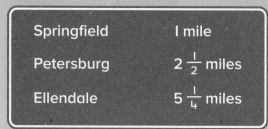

Springfield	I mile
Petersburg	$2\frac{1}{2}$ miles
Ellendale	$5\frac{1}{4}$ miles

Complete these statements.

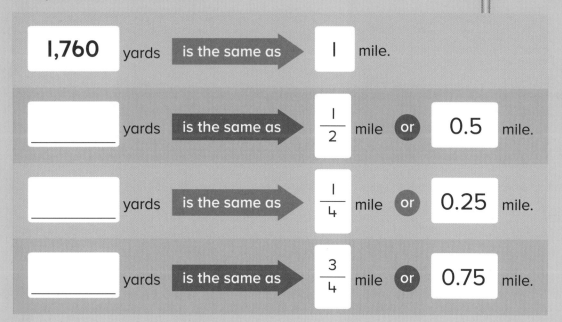

1,760 yards	is the same as	I mile.
_____ yards	is the same as	$\frac{1}{2}$ mile **or** 0.5 mile.
_____ yards	is the same as	$\frac{1}{4}$ mile **or** 0.25 mile.
_____ yards	is the same as	$\frac{3}{4}$ mile **or** 0.75 mile.

How could you figure out the
number of feet in one mile?

Step Up   I.   Convert between inches and feet to complete these.

a.   I7 inches = ___ ft ___ in

b.   32 inches = ___ ft ___ in

c.   I5 inches = ___ ft ___ in

d.   _____ inches = 2 ft 5 in

2. Convert between feet and yards to complete these.

a.

8 yd = _____ ft

b.

23 yd = _____ ft

c.

$4\frac{1}{2}$ yd = _____ ft

d.

_____ yd = 27 ft

e.

_____ yd = 45 ft

f.

19 yd = _____ ft

3. Solve each problem. Show your thinking.

a. Evan has a length of lumber that is exactly 3 yards long. He needs a piece that is 3 inches shorter. What length does he need?

_____ ft _____ in

b. Ramon and Dana meet at the park for a 3-mile run. Ramon runs home from the park so he actually runs an extra 175 yd. What total distance does Ramon run?

_____ yd

c. Half a mile of road is to be resurfaced. On the first day, 120 ft is completed. What length of road is still to be done?

_____ yd

d. High tide on Monday was 9.5 feet. Thursday's high tide was 3 inches less. What was the height of Thursday's high tide?

_____ ft

Step Ahead

The shortest person to play in the NBA measured 5 feet 3 inches. The tallest player measured 7 feet 7 inches.

What is the difference in their heights? _____ inches

Constructing and Interpreting a Line Plot (Involving Inches)

Read this experiment.

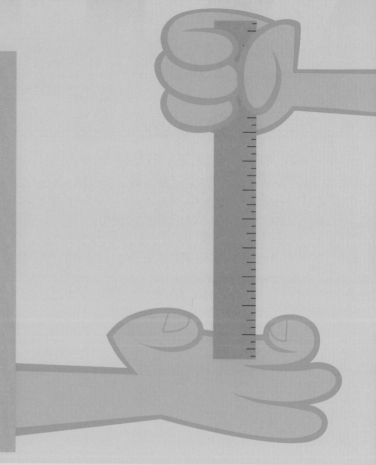

THE EXPERIMENT

Step 1

One student holds a foot long ruler by one end so that it hangs vertically.

Step 2

At the other end of the ruler, a second student places their thumb and forefinger about half an inch from either side of the ruler.

Step 3

When the student holding the ruler releases it without warning, the second student must try to catch it.

Step 4

The speed of the student's reaction is measured from 0 to where it is caught (rounded to the nearest $\frac{1}{2}$ inch).

Step Up

1. Work with another student to conduct the experiment ten times. Record **your** results in the table below.

Trial	Result		Trial	Result
1			6	
2			7	
3			8	
4			9	
5			10	

2. What was your best (shortest) result? _____

3. Survey each student in your class to find their best result. Make a tally chart on scrap paper to record each result.

4. Complete this line plot to show the data you collected in Question 3.

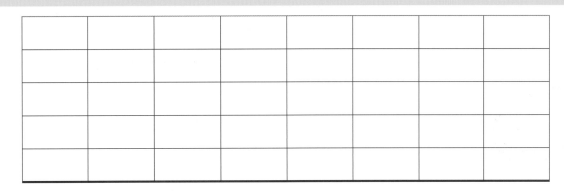

Reactions (inches)

5. a. Which result was recorded most frequently?

b. What was the difference between
your result and the most frequent class result?

c. Which result was recorded least frequently?

d. What was the shortest class result?

e. What was the longest class result?

f. What was the difference between the lengths
of the shortest and longest class results?

Step Ahead

Construct a line plot that shows
data to match **all** of these.

- 25 results

- $4\frac{1}{2}$ inches was the most
  frequent result

- 7 was the worst result

- $3\frac{1}{2}$ was the best result

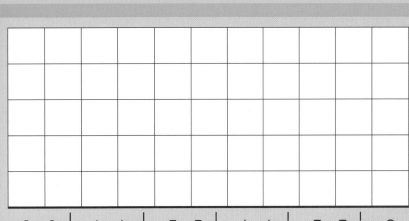

$$3 \quad 3\frac{1}{2} \quad 4 \quad 4\frac{1}{2} \quad 5 \quad 5\frac{1}{2} \quad 6 \quad 6\frac{1}{2} \quad 7 \quad 7\frac{1}{2} \quad 8$$

Reactions (inches)

Layla is planning a hike. How much farther
is Springwood Falls than Hard Rock Valley?

Hard Rock Valley   1.2 miles

Springwood Falls   3.9 miles

Springwood Falls is more
than double the distance.

Damon drew jumps on this number line
to figure out the exact difference.

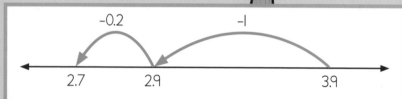

−0.2   −1

2.7   2.9   3.9

What steps did he follow? What is another way to find the difference?

Layla decides to buy some supplies.
How would you figure out the difference in cost between these two items?

Janice figured it out like this.

$7.99 − $2.45

$7.99 − $2 = $5.99
$5.99 − 40¢ = $5.59
$5.59 − 5¢ = $5.54

MAP
BOOK

$7.99

$2.45

What steps did Janice follow? What is another way to find the difference?

Step Up

1.   Draw jumps on the number line to figure out each difference.

a.

6.5 − 2.3 = ____

b.

7.8 − 4.1 = ____

2. Figure out the difference between these prices. Show your thinking.

a.  $3.50 $1.20

$ _____

b. $6.70 $5.30

$ _____

c. $8.40 $3.30

$ _____

d. $4.88 $1.32

$ _____

e. $5.75 $2.52

$ _____

f. $6.99 $3.47

$ _____

Step Ahead

A student used this number line to figure out 7.81 − 2.41.
Write the correct difference. Then explain the mistake that was made.

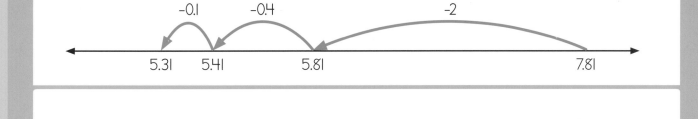

−0.1   −0.4   −2

5.31   5.41   5.81   7.81

_____

_____

Look at these performance scores.

How could you figure out the difference between Liam's score and Nina's score?

> I know that 12.4 is the same as 12.40.

TALENT QUEST

LEADER BOARD

Liam	12.4
Nina	15.92
Jacob	18.51
Mary	7.2

Lilly used this written method to figure out the difference. What steps did she follow?

$$
\begin{array}{r}
15.92 \\
-\ \ 0.40 \\
\hline
15.52 \\
-\ 12.00 \\
\hline
3.52
\end{array}
$$

What are some other differences that you can figure out? Record your thinking in the working space.

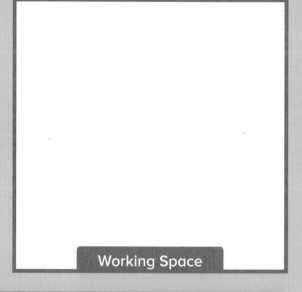

Working Space

Step Up

I. Figure out these differences. Show your thinking.

a.
8.60 − 5.1 = _____

b.
13.6 − 10.02 = _____

c.
14.92 − 10.3 = _____

2. Figure out the amount that is left in the wallet after each purchase.

a. $7.60 $3.50

$ _____

b. $15.95 $4.20

$ _____

c. $16.35 $5.20

$ _____

d. $9.75 $4.03

$ _____

e. $13.59 $2.47

$ _____

f. $19.55 $12.25

$ _____

g. $14.80 $3.00

$ _____

h. $17.88 $6.10

$ _____

i. $8.45 $5.03

$ _____

Step Ahead ▶ James has $20 in his wallet. He buys two of these meal deals. How much money does he have left over?

$ _____

SALAD BAR

Salad + drink

$7.95

Working Space

Using Written Methods to Subtract Decimal Fractions

How could you figure out the difference in mass between these two dogs?

14.2 kg   17.65 kg

It must be about 3 kg because 17 – 14 = 3.

These students figured it out like this.

Kylie	Juan	Megan
17.65 – 0.20 ───── 17.45 – 14.00 ───── 3.45	17.65 – 14.2 17 – 14 = 3 $\frac{65}{100} - \frac{20}{100} = \frac{45}{100}$ Difference is $3\frac{45}{100}$	17.65 – 14.2 ───── 3.45

What are the steps in each method? Whose method do you prefer? Why?

What other way could you calculate the difference?

How could you figure out the difference in cost between these two items?

$8.68 $3.25

The numbers are a bit "messy" so I would use a written method.

Step Up

1. Use Megan's method to figure out each difference.

a.

T	O	t	h
	7 . 8	6	
–	3 . 4	0	

b.

T	O	t	h
1	8 . 9	3	
–	6 . 5	1	

c.

T	O	t	h
2	4 . 0	7	
– 1	2 . 0	3	

2. Choose and use a written method to figure out the difference between each pair of weights.

a.

6.2 kg   9.85 kg

_____ kg

b.

7.64 kg   5.03 kg

_____ kg

c.

15.10 kg   27.2kg

_____ kg

d.

5.3 kg   28.7 kg

_____ kg

e.

8.07 kg   19.17 kg

_____ kg

f.

34.55 kg   13.05 kg

_____ kg

g.

10.4 kg   18.43 kg

_____ kg

h.

16.79 kg   5.29 kg

_____ kg

i.

3.88 kg   10.99 kg

_____ kg

Step Ahead

A student used the standard subtraction algorithm to figure out 16.45 – 3.2. Write the correct answer. Then explain the mistake that was made.

$$
\begin{array}{r}
1\ 6\ .\ 4\ 5 \\
-\quad\ \ 3\ .\ 2 \\
\hline
1\ 6\ 1\ .\ 3
\end{array}
$$

Subtracting Decimal Fractions Involving Tenths (Decomposing Ones)

What do you know about tides? Do tides occur at the same time each day? Look at this table.

Tide Chart				
Day	1st high	2nd high	1st low	2nd low
Monday	9.2 ft	8.4 ft	1.8 ft	0.9 ft
Wednesday	9.3 ft	8.1 ft	1.6 ft	0.8 ft

How could you figure out the difference between the first and second high tides on Monday?

The difference is small so I will count on from 8.4.

What is the difference between the first high and low tides on Wednesday?

Koda used a number line to find the difference like this.

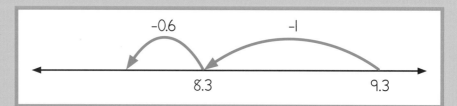

What steps did Koda follow?
What is the difference between the two tide levels?

Kana used the standard subtraction algorithm to figure out the difference between the second high tide and the second low tides on Wednesday.

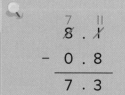

What steps did he follow? What does each red digit represent?

Step Up

1. Draw jumps on the number line to figure out each difference.

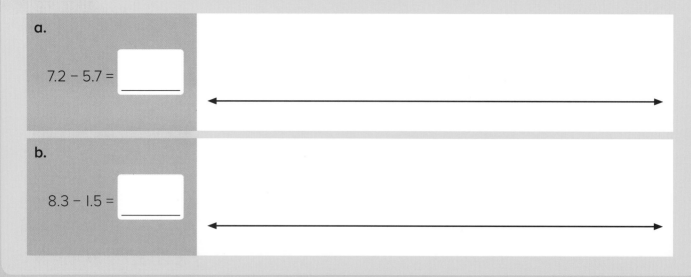

a.

7.2 − 5.7 = [   ]

b.

8.3 − 1.5 = [   ]

2. Figure out each difference. Draw jumps on the number line to show your thinking.

a.

$9.1 - 7.8 =$ _____

⟵──────────────────────────────⟶

b.

$5.4 - 0.9 =$ _____

⟵──────────────────────────────⟶

3. Choose and use a written method to figure out the difference between the tides.

a.	High tide 7.3 ft	Low tide 1.6 ft	b.	High tide 8.2 ft	Low tide 1.9 ft

_____ ft   _____ ft

Step Ahead High tide on Monday was 0.4 ft more than on Tuesday. Thursday's tide was 9.1 ft. This was 0.3 ft more than on Monday but 0.2 ft less than on Sunday.

Figure out the height of the tide on each day.

Monday _____ ft

Tuesday _____ ft

Thursday _____ ft

Sunday _____ ft

Working Space

Subtracting Decimal Fractions Involving Hundredths (Decomposing Tenths)

Kimie jumped 4.85 meters in the long jump event at school.
Logan jumped 0.97 meters less than Kimie. Mia jumped 0.29 meters less than Kimie.

How could you figure out the length of Logan's jump?

I would count back and adjust my answer like this.

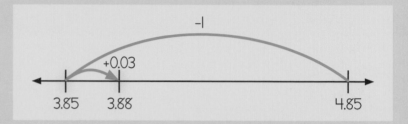

Draw jumps on this number line to show how you could figure out the length of Mia's jump.

These three written methods were used to figure out the length of Mia's jump.

What are the steps for each method? Complete the calculations.

$4.85 - 0.09 = 4.76$

$4.76 - 0.20 =$ _____

Difference is _____

Which method do you prefer? Why?

$4.85 - 0.29$

$4 - 0 = 4$

$\dfrac{85}{100} - \dfrac{}{100} = \dfrac{}{100}$

Difference is _____

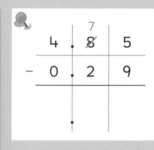

1.   Paige jumped 1.80 meters short of this long-jump record.

Record
5.54 m

Write a number sentence to show how far Paige jumped.
Then draw jumps on the number line to show how you figured it out.

_____ − _____ = _____

2. Draw jumps on the number line to figure out each difference.

a.

$7.65 - 3.26 =$ _____

<-->

b.

$9.20 - 7.85 =$ _____

<-->

3. Choose and use a written method to figure out each difference.

a.

$8.46 - 3.18 =$ _____

b.

$9.35 - 5.72 =$ _____

c.

$15.82 - 12.09 =$ _____

d.

$18.03 - 10.85 =$ _____

e.

$10.72 - 4.27 =$ _____

f.

$21.58 - 17.53 =$ _____

Step Ahead

Imagine you have this money and you buy both items.
How much money will you have left?

$ _____

$8.75 $17.95

Subtracting Decimal Fractions (Decomposing Multiple Places)

This thermometer shows the temperature at different times in one morning.

How does the temperature change?

What are some temperature changes that you could figure out in your head?

11 a.m.   53.09°F

10 a.m.   49.32°F

7 a.m.   42.3°F

12 noon   55.7°F

8 a.m.   44.7°F

I can easily figure out the difference between 44.7 and 55.7.

What was the change in temperature between 10 a.m. and 8 a.m.? How do you know?

Noah decided to use the standard subtraction algorithm to calculate the difference. Complete his calculation below.

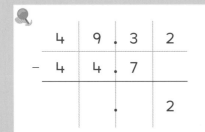

	4	9 . 3	2
−	4	4 . 7	
		.	2

Does it change the answer if you show 44.7 as 44.70?

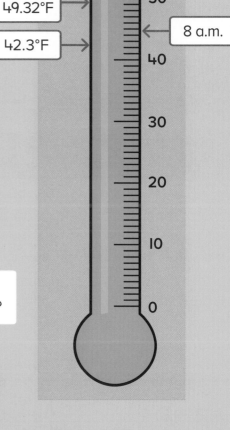

Step Up

1. Use the thermometer above to figure out the temperature change between these times.

a. 11 a.m. to 12 noon

_____ °F

b. 10 a.m. to 11 a.m.

_____ °F

2. Figure out each difference. Show your thinking.

a.
32.30 − 19.8 = _____

b.
18.37 − 12.9 = _____

c.
25.02 − 10.4 = _____

d.
14.5 − 9.07 = _____

e.
28.3 − 15.72 = _____

f.
16.04 − 0.9 = _____

g.
24.3 − 17.24 = _____

h.
16.79 − 5.73 = _____

i.
12.88 − 10.99 = _____

Step Ahead ▶ Solve these word problems.

a. It is 45.03°F in Tacoma, WA.
The temperature in Olympia is 0.2°F less.
What is the temperature in Olympia?

_____ °F

b. It was 48.50°F outside. The temperature
dropped 0.8°F over the next hour.
What is the new temperature?

_____ °F

Which package is heavier? How do you know?

About how much is the difference?

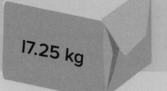

17.25 kg   5.6 kg

The difference between 17 and 5 is 12, so the first package is about 12 kg heavier.

How could you figure out the exact difference?

Deon followed these steps.

What steps did he follow?

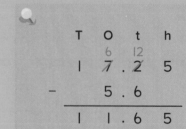

```
      T   O  t   h
          6  12
      1   7 . 2   5
  -       5 . 6
  ────────────────
      1   1 . 6   5
```

Step Up   I.   For each of these, use Deon's method to figure out the difference in mass.

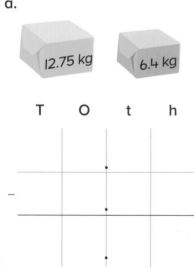

a.

12.75 kg   6.4 kg

T   O   t   h

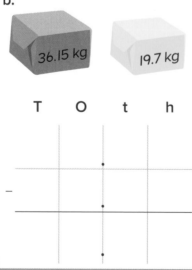

b.

36.15 kg   19.7 kg

T   O   t   h

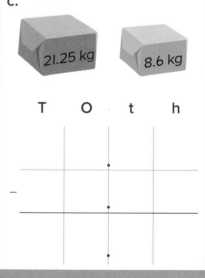

c.

21.25 kg   8.6 kg

T   O   t   h

164

2. Calculate the difference in mass between these sacks of grain. Record the steps you use.

a.

16.45 kg   8.25 kg

_____ kg

b.

8.35 kg   5.75 kg

_____ kg

c.

2.65 kg   8.25 kg

_____ kg

d.

8.8 kg   7.9 kg

_____ kg

e.

17.5 kg   8.6 kg

_____ kg

f.

8.45 kg   12.8 kg

_____ kg

g.

17.6 kg   3.85 kg

_____ kg

h.

2.05 kg   8.4 kg

_____ kg

i.

3.7 kg   12.25 kg

_____ kg

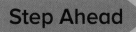

Step Ahead Write a mass in each box to make the balance pictures true.

a.

6.8 kg   15.03 kg

b.

5.43 kg   17.9 kg

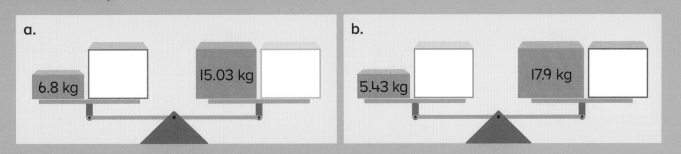

Introducing the Coordinate Plane and Plotting Ordered Pairs

This picture shows a plan of a model town.

Each star represents a tree and each circle represents a car. The plan is drawn on a coordinate plane.

A **coordinate plane** is a rectangular grid which has a horizontal axis called the *x-axis* and a vertical axis called the *y-axis*. The **origin** is where the axes meet.

Two numbers that describe a specific point on a coordinate plane are known as an **ordered pair**. These numbers may also be called **coordinates**.

The first number in an ordered pair tells the distance to move from the origin along the *x-axis*. The second coordinate tells the distance to move up the *y-axis*.

Where is the origin on this coordinate plane? What are the coordinates of the origin?

What is located at the coordinates (4, 15)?

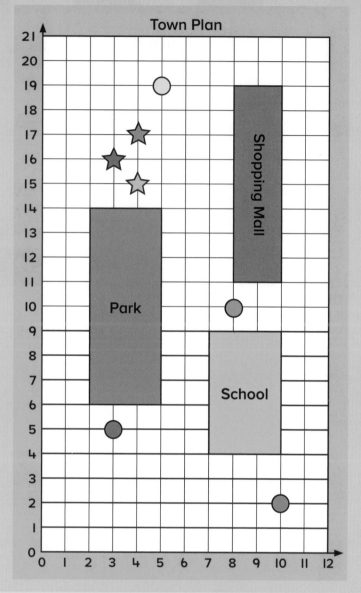

Town Plan

Step Up   Look at the coordinate plane above.

1. Write the coordinates and the color of each car.

Car color	red			
Coordinates	(8, 10)			

2. Write the coordinates of the four corners of the school and the park.

School				
Park				

3. This table gives the coordinates of three corners of rectangular buildings in a different part of the same town. Mark the three corners on the grid below. Write the coordinates of the 4th corner in the table. Then shade the buildings on the grid.

Bank	(3, 4)	(3, 8)	(7, 8)	_____
Hotel	(8, 7)	(8, 11)	(12, 11)	_____
Hospital	(14, 10)	(19, 10)	(19, 6)	_____

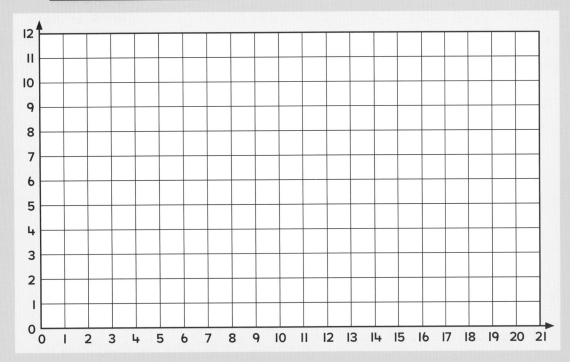

4. Mark the location of these three cars on the coordinate plane above using the information given. Make sure they are not on a building. Then complete the ordered pair for each location.

Car color	red	blue	green
Coordinates	(14, ____)	(____ , 8)	(3, ____)

Step Ahead

Use the model at the top of page 166. Here are the beginnings of instructions to move the red car from between the school and the shopping mall to the other side of the park. Continue and complete the instructions in the same way.

Start at (8, 10). Move to (____ , ____). Then move to _____

_____ Finally move to (1, 10).

Identifying Relationships Between Two Numerical Patterns

Look at this growing pattern.
What do you notice?

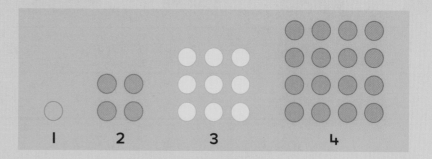

What numbers should be written in the second row of this table to describe the pattern?

Picture number	1	2	3	4	5	6	7
Total number of counters							

How did you figure out the numbers to write in the table?

What do you notice about the number you wrote for each picture?

Step Up

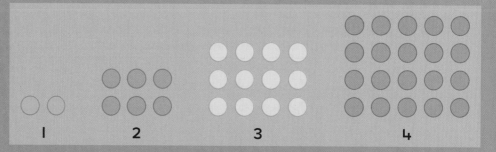

I. Look at the pictures in this growing pattern.

a. Complete the table below to show the total number of counters in each picture of this pattern.

Picture number	1	2	3	4	5	6	7
Total number of counters	2						

b. How did you figure out the numbers to keep the pattern going?

2. Look at the pictures in this growing pattern.

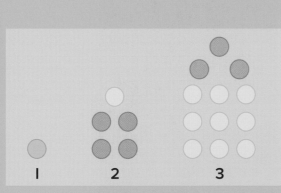

a. Complete the table below to show the total number of counters in each picture of this pattern.

Picture number	1	2	3	4	5	6	7
Total number of counters	1						

b. Look at the number of counters for each picture in Question 1a and 2a.
How are the patterns related?

Step Ahead

This pattern of "houses with roofs" was made by joining the shape in the pattern above and the shape in the pattern at the top of page 168. The first row of the table matches the number rows of counters in the square part of the "house".

a. Sketch the next picture that you would see in the pattern.

b. Complete the table below to show the total number of counters in the pictures of this pattern.

Picture number	1	2	3	4	5	6	7
Total number of counters	1						

Generating and Graphing Ordered Pairs from Two Numerical Patterns

This growing pattern was made with toothpicks.

| 1 | 2 | 3 | 4 |

What do you notice?
What patterns do you see?

Complete this table to match the pattern.

Picture number	1	2	3	4
Number of squares	1	2		
Number of toothpicks	4	7		

What ordered pairs should they write to show the pattern?

Marking ordered pairs on a coordinate plane is called graphing or plotting.

How would you graph the ordered pairs on the coordinate plane?

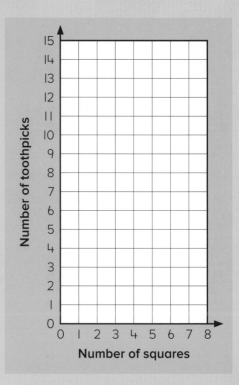

Number of toothpicks / Number of squares

Step Up

1. Look at this pattern made with toothpicks.

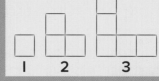

| 1 | 2 | 3 |

a. Complete the table. If necessary, draw more pictures on scrap paper.

Picture number	1	2	3	4	5
Number of squares	1				
Number of toothpicks	4				

b. Use the numbers for each picture to write ordered pairs.

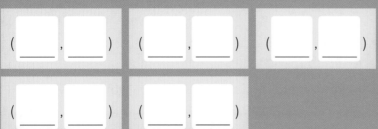

(____ , ____) (____ , ____) (____ , ____)

(____ , ____) (____ , ____)

c. Graph the ordered pairs on the coordinate plane.

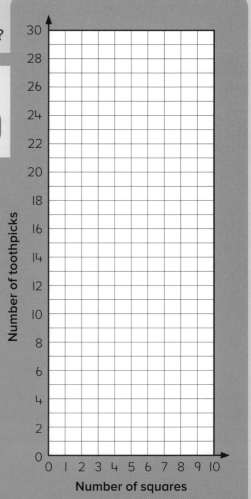

Number of toothpicks / Number of squares

2. Look at this pattern made with toothpicks.

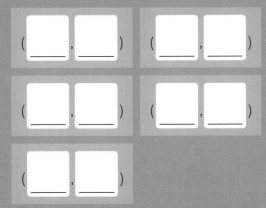

a. Complete the table. If necessary, draw more pictures on scrap paper.

Picture number	1	2	3	4	5
Number of triangles	1				
Number of toothpicks	3				

b. Use the numbers for each picture to write the ordered pairs.

(_____ , _____) (_____ , _____)

(_____ , _____) (_____ , _____)

(_____ , _____)

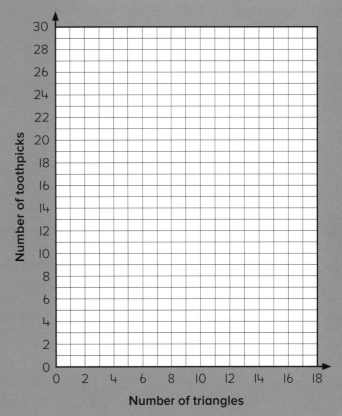

c. Graph the ordered pairs in blue on the coordinate plane.

d. Use a pattern to figure out the ordered pairs for Picture 6 and Picture 7. Then graph the points on the coordinate plane.

Step Ahead

Write the first four ordered pairs for this sequence of triangle pictures made with toothpicks. Use red to plot the points on the coordinate plane above.

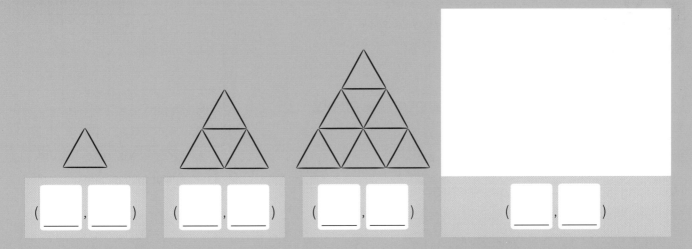

(_____ , _____) (_____ , _____) (_____ , _____) (_____ , _____)

Representing Real-World Data on a Coordinate Plane

Lela has saved $10. She plans to save $2 each week.

How could she show the amount she will save in 10 weeks?

She could use a table.

Number of weeks	0	1	2		
Amount saved	10	12			

She could use ordered pairs.

(_____ , _____)   (_____ , _____)   (_____ , _____)

(_____ , _____)   (_____ , _____)

A graph on a coordinate plane is a good way to show how the savings grow.

Lela started with $10. Where is that point on the graph?
What ordered pair matches that point?

What do you notice about all the points?

How long will it take Lela to save $40?
How do you know?

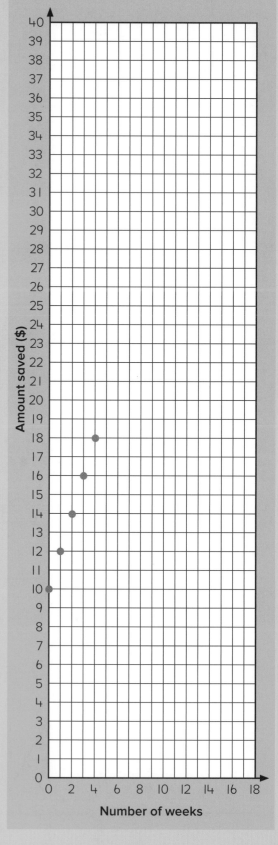

Amount saved ($)

Number of weeks

I. Olivia has saved $36. She plans to **spend** $6 every three weeks.

a. Complete this table to show the amount she has at the start and after every three weeks until the money is spent.

Number of weeks	0	3	6	9			
Amount left ($)	36						

b. Write ordered pairs to match.

(0 , 36) (3 , ___) (___ , ___) (___ , ___)

(___ , ___) (___ , ___) (___ , ___)

c. Use blue to graph the ordered pairs on the coordinate plane on page 172.

2. Alex has saved $40. He plans to spend $5 every two weeks.

a. Write ordered pairs to show the amount at the start and after every two weeks until the money is spent.

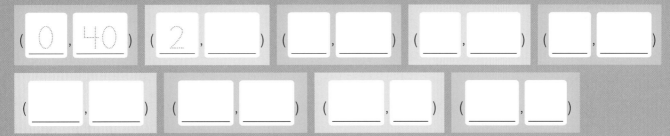

(0 , 40) (2 , ___) (___ , ___) (___ , ___) (___ , ___)

(___ , ___) (___ , ___) (___ , ___) (___ , ___)

b. Use red to graph the ordered pairs on the coordinate plane on page 172.

Look at the blue and red points on the coordinate plane on page 172. Write about what do you notice.

_____

_____

_____

_____

_____

Interpreting Coordinate Values for Real-World Situations

Ashley, Rita, and Dixon are siblings. They were all born in January but in different years. The blue points show Ashley's and Rita's ages on April 4 in three consecutive years.

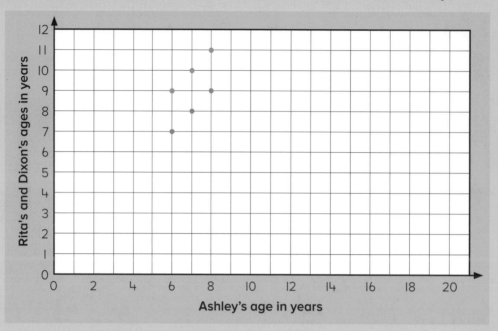

What do you notice about the points for the Ashley and Rita?

What ordered pairs would you write for the three points that match Ashley's and Rita's ages? What ordered pair would you write for Ashley and Rita at their next birthday?

How do the ages of Ashley and Rita compare?

How old will Rita be when Ashley is 15 years old? How do you know?

If you know Ashley's age, how could you figure out Rita's age?

Does it make sense to join the ordered pairs that show Ashley's and Rita's ages?

Step Up

1. The red points on the coordinate plane above show Ashley's and Dixon's ages on April 4 in three consecutive years.

   a. What ordered pairs would you write for the three points?

   (____ , ____)   (____ , ____)   (____ , ____)

   b. If you know Ashley's age, how could you figure out Dixon's age?

   _____

   _____

2. The blue points show how Blake saves.

a. How much did Blake have when he started to save?

$ _____

b. Write the ordered pairs that match the blue points.

(_____ , _____)   (_____ , _____)

(_____ , _____)   (_____ , _____)

c. Complete these ordered pairs to show how Blake continues to save.

(12 , _____)   (13 , _____)   (14 , _____)

3. The red points show how Sheree saves.

a. How much did Sheree have when she started to save?

$ _____

b. Write the ordered pairs that match the red points.

(_____ , _____)   (_____ , _____)

(_____ , _____)   (_____ , _____)

c. Complete these ordered pairs to show how Sheree continues to save.

(6 , _____)   (7 , _____)   (8 , _____)

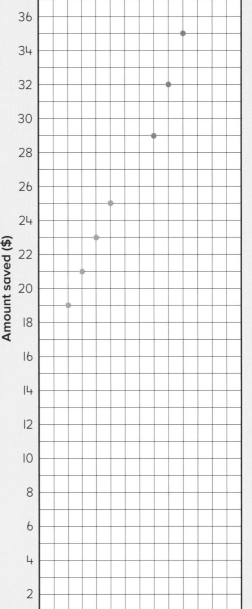

Step Ahead   Look at the coordinate plane above. Draw a line to connect the blue points and another line to connect the red points. What do you notice?

_____

_____

8.1   Reviewing Division Strategies

Lora bought a cell phone for $369.
She paid for it in three equal monthly payments.

How could you figure out the amount she paid each month?

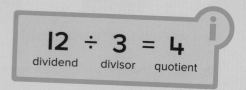

$$12 \div 3 = 4$$
dividend   divisor   quotient

Rita used a sharing strategy. What do the blocks represent?

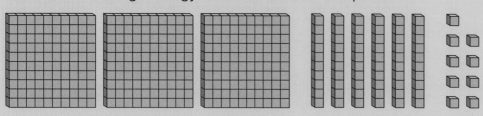

How could you share these blocks into three equal groups?

Loop the blocks to show the amount in each share.

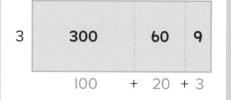

I'll call the amount that is paid each month P.
$P = 369 \div 3$

Mika used a different strategy. He followed these steps.

Step 1	Step 2	Step 3
He drew a rectangle to show the problem. The length of one side becomes the unknown value.	He split the rectangle into parts so that it was easier to divide by 3.	He thought: $3 \times 100 = 300$ $3 \times 20 = 60$ $3 \times 3 = 9$

Step 1: 3 | 369 | P

Step 2: 3 | 300 | 60 | 9

Step 3: 3 | 300 | 60 | 9   100 + 20 + 3

Why did he choose the numbers 300, 60, and 9?

Why did he add 100 + 20 + 3?

To find the amount, Rita thinks $369 \div 3 = P$ and Mika thinks $3 \times P = 369$.

How much did Lora pay each month?

How could you use these strategies to calculate $484 \div 4$?

Step Up Use a strategy of your choice to complete each of these. Show your thinking.

a.

$693 \div 3 = $ _____

b.

$530 \div 5 = $ _____

c.

$742 \div 7 = $ _____

d.

$612 \div 6 = $ _____

e.

$3{,}906 \div 3 = $ _____

f.

$8{,}420 \div 4 = $ _____

Step Ahead Break each number into parts that are easy to **divide by 5**.

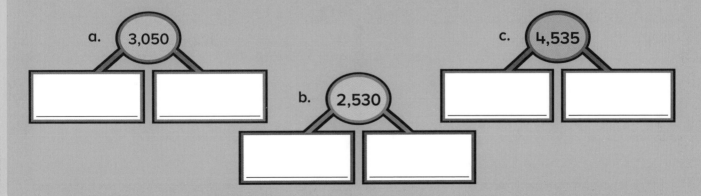

a. 3,050

b. 2,530

c. 4,535

8.2 ▸ Partitioning and Regrouping Dividends

Imagine you are planning a vacation.

How can you figure out the cost of one night at this hotel?

David showed the total cost using base-10 blocks.

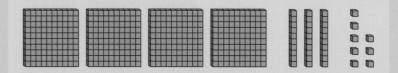

Then he followed these steps to calculate the cost of each night.

	Step 1	Step 2	Step 3
	Share the hundreds.	Share the tens.	Share the ones.
3 Nights			

What did David do at each step?

What is the cost of each night?

What is another way you could figure it out?

Step Up

1. Draw or write the amount in each share. Use blocks to help you.

a.	456 ÷ 3
Shares	

b.	372 ÷ 3
Shares	

2. Use a strategy of your choice to complete each of these. You can use blocks to help. Show your thinking.

a.
$620 \div 5 = \underline{\hspace{2cm}}$

b.
$375 \div 3 = \underline{\hspace{2cm}}$

c.
$528 \div 4 = \underline{\hspace{2cm}}$

d.
$429 \div 3 = \underline{\hspace{2cm}}$

e.
$4{,}206 \div 3 = \underline{\hspace{2cm}}$

f.
$3{,}250 \div 5 = \underline{\hspace{2cm}}$

Step Ahead   Look at the example below. Write two other ways to split 960 into parts to make it easy to divide by 4.

$960 \div 4$

is the same as

$(800 \div 4) + (160 \div 4)$

a.
$960 \div 4$

is the same as

_____

b.
$960 \div 4$

is the same as

_____

8.3 ▶ Recording Division

Three people share the cost of renting this car.

How could you figure out each person's share?

Anna showed the total cost with blocks then followed these steps to figure out each share.

$348 per week

	Step 1	Step 2	Step 3
	Share the hundreds.	Share the tens.	Share the ones.
Shares	▦	▮	▫▫▫▫▫▫
	▦	▮	▫▫▫▫▫▫
	▦	▮	▫▫▫▫▫▫

Carlos followed these steps to help him write the amount in each share.

	Step 1	Step 2	Step 3
	Share the hundreds.	Share the tens.	Share the ones.
Shares	100	100 + 10	100 + 10 + 6
	100	100 + 10	100 + 10 + 6
	100	100 + 10	100 + 10 + 6

How much is each person's share of the car rental?

Step Up

1. Figure out how much two people, then four people would pay to share the same total cost of the car rental above. Use a strategy of your choice.

a. $348 ÷ 2

Shares

b. $348 ÷ 4

Shares

180

2. Figure out the amount in each share. You can use blocks to help your thinking.

a.
$512 ÷ 4 = $ _____

| 100 |
| 100 |
| 100 |
| 100 |

b.
$798 ÷ 6 = $ _____

c.
$847 ÷ 7 = $ _____

d.
$732 ÷ 6 = $ _____

e.
$648 ÷ 4 = $ _____

f.
$573 ÷ 3 = $ _____

g.
$4,230 ÷ 3 = $ _____

| 1,000 |
| 1,000 |
| 1,000 |

h.
$5,631 ÷ 3 = $ _____

Step Ahead For each of these, write a digit to complete a three-digit number that you can divide without any amount left over. Then write the answers.

| 5 | 8 | ___ | ÷ 3 = _____ |

| 6 | 2 | ___ | ÷ 5 = _____ |

| 6 | ___ | 8 | ÷ 4 = _____ |

| 7 | ___ | 9 | ÷ 3 = _____ |

Developing the Standard Division Algorithm

Four people shared the cost of a restaurant bill for $84.

Gavin calculated each share and recorded his thinking like this.

How much did each person pay?

4 people share $84
2 tens + 1 one
2 tens + 1 one
2 tens + 1 one
2 tens + 1 one

Another way to record the calculation is to use a division bracket.

What numbers are written around the division bracket?
What does each number tell you?

$$4 \overline{)8 \quad 4}$$

What is happening in each of these steps?
How are they similar to Gavin's method?

Step 1

T	O
2	

$$4 \overline{)8 \quad | \quad 4}$$

Step 2

T	O
2	1

$$4 \overline{)8 \quad | \quad 4}$$

Look at these steps to figure out 906 shared by 3.

Step 1

H	T	O
3		

$$3 \overline{)9 \quad | \quad 0 \quad | \quad 6}$$

Step 2

H	T	O
3	0	

$$3 \overline{)9 \quad | \quad 0 \quad | \quad 6}$$

Step 3

H	T	O
3	0	2

$$3 \overline{)9 \quad | \quad 0 \quad | \quad 6}$$

What is happening in each step?
Why is 0 written above the bracket in Step 2?

I think I could skip Step 1 because I know that 90 tens divided by 3 is 30 tens.

Numbers in equations are arranged in different positions when using division brackets.

$$64 \div 2 = 32 \qquad 2 \overline{)6 \quad 4}^{\,3 \quad 2}$$

1. Rewrite each equation using the division bracket.

a.

68 ÷ 2 = 34

```
        T   O
      ____|____
    )    |
```

b.

32 = 96 ÷ 3

```
        T   O
      ____|____
    )    |
```

c.

412 = 824 ÷ 2

```
      H   T   O
    __|___|___
  )  |   |
```

d.

309 ÷ 3 = 103

```
      H   T   O
    __|___|___
  )  |   |
```

2. Use the steps on page 182 to calculate each quotient.

a.
```
    T | O
  ___|___
2 ) 8 | 2
```

b.
```
    T | O
  ___|___
3 ) 6 | 3
```

c.
```
    T | O
  ___|___
5 ) 5 | 5
```

d.
```
    T | O
  ___|___
4 ) 8 | 4
```

e.
```
   H | T | O
  ___|___|___
3 ) 6 | 9 | 3
```

f.
```
  Th | H | T | O
  ___|___|___|___
2 ) 8 | 6 | 2 | 6
```

g.
```
   H | T | O
  ___|___|___
4 ) 8 | 0 | 4
```

h.
```
   H | T | O
  ___|___|___
2 ) 4 | 6 | 0
```

i.
```
  Th | H | T | O
  ___|___|___|___
4 ) 4 | 0 | 4 | 8
```

j.
```
  Th | H | T | O
  ___|___|___|___
3 ) 9 | 3 | 0 | 9
```

3. Choose three problems from Question 2. Rewrite each as an equation.

Write digits to complete each problem.

a.
```
      Th | H | T | O
         | 1 | 3 | 2 | 0
      _____
    3 )    | 9 |   |
```

b.
```
      Th | H | T | O
         | 3 | 4 | 0 |
      _____
    )    | 6 | 8 |   | 2
```

8.5 Introducing the Standard Division Algorithm

Three friends equally share $78.

Jacob used blocks and wrote this to figure out each share.

How much is each share?

What regrouping did Jacob have to do? How do you know?

78 ÷ 3
7 tens ÷ 3 = 2 tens
and 1 ten left over
18 ones ÷ 3 = 6 ones

**Tia tried using the division bracket but did not know
how to show the regrouping.**

Emily showed her the standard division algorithm to help.

```
    T   O
    2
3 ) 7   8
```

Step 1		T O
Divide		2
There are 7 tens to share. There are 3 shares. There are 2 tens in each share because 3 × 2 is 6.		3) 7 8

Step 2		T O
Multiply then subtract.		2

There are 7 tens to share.
There are 6 tens shared.
There is 1 ten left over
because 7 − 6 is 1.
		3) 7 8
		  − 6
		    1

Step 3		T O
Bring down the next digit.		2

There is 1 ten left to share.
There are 8 ones to share.
That makes 18 ones
to share.
		3) 7 8
		  − 6 ↓
		    1 8

Emily completed the
standard algorithm by
repeating the first two
steps with 18 ones.

```
    T   O
    2   6
3 ) 7   8
  − 6   ↓
    1   8
  −     1   8
        0
```

How is Emily's method similar to Jacob's method?

What is another method you could use?

Try using the standard division algorithm to calculate 68 ÷ 4.

Use the standard division algorithm to calculate each quotient.
Remember to estimate before or after your calculation to check your accuracy.

a.	T	O
4)	5	6

b.	T	O
3)	8	1

c.	T	O
5)	8	5

d.	T	O
2)	7	6

e.	T	O
6)	8	4

f.	T	O
3)	7	8

g.	T	O
7)	9	1

h.	T	O
3)	5	4

i.	T	O
8)	9	6

j.	T	O
4)	9	2

k.	T	O
5)	7	5

l.	T	O
3)	4	8

> **Step Ahead**

Show two different ways to figure out 87 ÷ 3.

Working with the Standard Division Algorithm

A rope measured 645 centimeters. It was cut into three equal parts.

How would you figure out the length of each part?

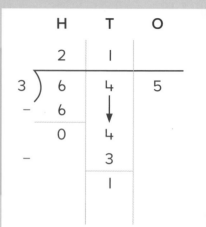

Megan decided to use the standard division algorithm to calculate each length.

What steps has she completed?
What does she need to do next?

Complete Megan's calculation.

Four wheels cost $832. How much does each wheel cost?

Kimie followed these steps to figure it out.

8 hundreds divided by 4	3 tens divided by 4	32 ones divided by 4
2 hundreds	2 hundreds + 0 tens	2 hundreds + 0 tens + 8 ones
2 hundreds	2 hundreds + 0 tens	2 hundreds + 0 tens + 8 ones
2 hundreds	2 hundreds + 0 tens	2 hundreds + 0 tens + 8 ones
2 hundreds	2 hundreds + 0 tens	2 hundreds + 0 tens + 8 ones

Corey and Sofia each used the standard algorithm.

Compare their calculations.

What do you notice about the steps Sofia used?

Why do you think she brought down the 3 tens and 2 ones at the same time?

Did this affect the final answer?

How does each method relate to Kimie's method?

Five friends ran a carwash. They earned $285 and split the money evenly.

How much was in each share?

How could you use the standard division algorithm to help you?

Complete these calculations using the standard division algorithm.

a.
H	T	O

$3 \overline{\smash{)}\ 4\quad 8\quad 6}$

b.
H	T	O

$4 \overline{\smash{)}\ 9\quad 0\quad 4}$

c.
H	T	O

$5 \overline{\smash{)}\ 4\quad I\quad 5}$

d.
Th	H	T	O

$4 \overline{\smash{)}\ 6\quad I\quad 8\quad 4}$

e.
Th	H	T	O

$6 \overline{\smash{)}\ I\quad 8\quad 7\quad 2}$

f.
Th	H	T	O

$5 \overline{\smash{)}\ 3\quad 2\quad 0\quad 5}$

Step Ahead

Choose two problems above that you can solve easily **without** using the standard division algorithm. Show your methods.

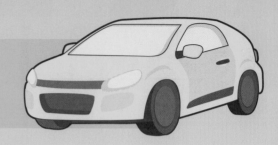

Mia plans to buy a car for $6,560.
She will make 40 equal payments to pay the total cost.

How could you figure out the amount of each payment?

Tyler used the standard division algorithm. He started like this.

What has he done in this part of his calculation?

Why do you think he did that?

6 thousands blocks can't be divided into 40 parts so he regrouped the 6 thousands as hundreds from the start.

	Th	H	T	O
		1		
40)	6	5	6	0
−	4	0		
	2	5		

What has he done in this part of his calculation?

Why did he write 240 on the fourth line under the division bracket?

He needed to divide 256 tens by 40. What did he multiply 40 by to make a product close to 256?

	Th	H	T	O
		1	6	
40)	6	5	6	0
−	4	0		
	2	5	6	
−	2	4	0	
		1	6	

Complete Tyler's calculation.

Franco decided to break a number into parts to divide.

How do you think he split 6,560?

He might have split it so that one part was 4,000. That would be an easy way to start.

I. Complete each sentence.

a.
[____] × 50 = 3,500

(so) 3,500 ÷ 50 = [____]

b.
[____] × 40 = 3,200

(so) 3,200 ÷ 40 = [____]

c.
[____] × 70 = 2,100

(so) 2,100 ÷ 70 = [____]

2. Use a method of your choice to solve each problem. Show your thinking.

a.
4,290 ÷ 30 = [____]

b.
4,250 ÷ 50 = [____]

c.
5,760 ÷ 30 = [____]

d.
7,590 ÷ 30 = [____]

e.
7,560 ÷ 60 = [____]

f.
5,720 ÷ 40 = [____]

Write the missing numbers on this trail.

60 → ×4 → [____] → ×10 → [____] → ÷40 → [____]

8.8 ▶ Converting Between Centimeters and Meters

Choose the number below that is likely to match an adult's arm span.

0.85 m   1.65 m

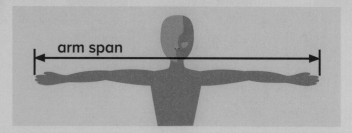

arm span

Why did you choose that number?

How would you describe the arm span in centimeters?

What is another way you could describe and write that length?

You could write it as a mixed number.

Complete this diagram to make a true statement.

| 1.65 m | is the same length as | _____ cm | is the same length as | $1\dfrac{}{100}$ m |

How could you use the diagram to help you to describe or write 25 centimeters in different ways?

How would you write 1.7 meters in centimeters and as a fraction of a meter?

Step Up ▶

1. Convert each length to centimeters. Then write it as a fraction of a meter.

a.
0.32 m = ☐ cm = ☐ m

b.
0.9 m = ☐ cm = ☐ m

c.
0.4 m = ☐ cm = ☐ m

d.
1.45 m = ☐ cm = ☐ m

e.
0.06 m = ☐ cm = ☐ m

f.
0.87 m = ☐ cm = ☐ m

2. Convert each length to meters. Then write it as a fraction of a meter.

a. ☐/☐ m = 14 cm = ☐ m

b. ☐/☐ m = 79 cm = ☐ m

c. ☐/☐ m = 115 cm = ☐ m

d. ☐/☐ m = 235 cm = ☐ m

e. ☐/☐ m = 160 cm = ☐ m

f. ☐/☐ m = 80 cm = ☐ m

3. Complete the missing parts to make these true.

a. ☐/☐ m = ☐/☐ cm = $2\frac{3}{10}$ m

b. 0.6 m = ☐/☐ cm = ☐ m

c. ☐/☐ m = 19 cm = ☐ m

d. ☐/☐ m = ☐/☐ cm = $\frac{3}{10}$ m

e. 3.05 m = ☐/☐ cm = ☐ m

f. ☐/☐ m = 211 cm = ☐ m

4. Write these lengths as a fraction of a meter. Then write the same fraction another way.

a. 125 cm = ☐ m = ☐ m

b. 275 cm = ☐ m = ☐ m

Step Ahead ▸ Choose the number that makes the most sense to complete the sentence.

a.

0.4 $\frac{1}{4}$ 0.04

The book is _____ m thick.

b.

$1\frac{5}{10}$ 1.5   150

Cody can stand and leap _____ cm.

Converting Between Millimeters and Centimeters

Where would 15 mm and 5 mm be on this number line? How do you know?

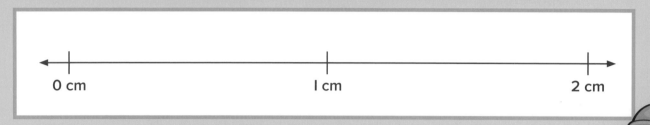

0 cm   1 cm   2 cm

Label each length above the number line.

How would you write these lengths as decimal fractions of a centimeter?

Label each length as a decimal fraction of a centimeter below the number line.

What is another way you can describe or write 15 mm?

Write a decimal fraction and a mixed number
to complete a true statement.

> I could write it as a mixed number.

| 15 mm | is the same length as | _____ cm | is the same length as | cm |

What are some different ways to write 250 mm?

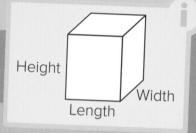

Height

Length   Width

Step Up   Use these boxes to answer Question 1
below and Question 2 on page 193.

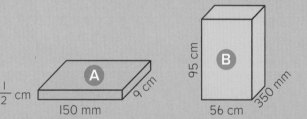

$\frac{1}{2}$ cm   A   9 cm

150 mm

95 cm   B   350 mm

56 cm

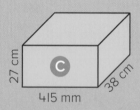

27 cm   C   38 cm

415 mm

6 mm   D   2.3 cm

$4\frac{1}{2}$ cm

1. Complete the tables to show the dimensions of the first two packages.

A

Length	Width	Height
mm	mm	mm
cm	cm	cm

B

Length	Width	Height
mm	mm	mm
cm	cm	cm

2. Use the dimensions of the boxes on page 192 to complete these.

C

Length	Width	Height
mm	mm	mm
cm	cm	cm

D

Length	Width	Height
mm	mm	mm
cm	cm	cm

3. Write numbers to show equivalent lengths.
Use decimal fractions and mixed numbers where necessary.

a.
25 mm = ☐ cm = ☐ cm

b.
☐ mm = 6.5 cm = ☐ cm

c.
☐ mm = ☐ cm = $3\frac{1}{2}$ cm

d.
45 mm = ☐ cm = ☐ cm

e.
5 mm = ☐ cm = ☐ cm

f.
☐ mm = ☐ cm = $\frac{1}{10}$ cm

4. Convert these lengths.

a.
☐ cm (=) 67 mm

b.
215 cm (=) ☐ mm

c.
☐ cm (=) 70 mm

d.
64 cm (=) ☐ mm

Step Ahead ▶ One meter of ribbon has been used to wrap this gift.
Write some possible dimensions of the box.
Allow 15 cm for the bow.

Height _____ cm   Width _____ mm

Working Space

This number line represents one meter.

0

What number would you write at the other end if you marked the line in centimeters?

What would you write at the other end if you marked the line in millimeters?

Where would you draw an arrow to show the length that is 50 cm long?
Use your ruler to determine the halfway mark and label the point.

What are all the different ways you could describe and write that length?

You could describe the length in millimeters, and
as a fraction of a meter, which could be written
as a decimal fraction or common fraction.

Complete this equivalence statement to show the different ways.

| 50 cm | is the same length as | _____ m | is the same length as | _____ m | is the same length as | _____ mm |

What are some different ways you could read 0.5 m?

Step Up

1. Write each length as a fraction of a meter. Use decimal fractions and common fractions.

a.
100 mm = 0._____ m = [   ] m

b.
10 mm = 0._____ m = [   ] m

c.
1 mm = 0._____ m = [   ] m

d.
75 mm = 0._____ m = [   ] m

e.
32 mm = 0._____ m = [   ] m

f.
91 mm = 0._____ m = [   ] m

2. Measure each strip. Write the length in millimeters and as a decimal fraction of a meter.

a.

_____ mm _____ m

b.

_____ mm _____ m

c.

_____ mm _____ m

d.

_____ mm _____ m

e.

_____ mm _____ m

f.

_____ mm _____ m

3. a. Add the length of each strip in Question 2. Then write the total in millimeters and meters.

The total length is _____ mm which is the same as _____ m.

b. Figure out the difference between the **longest** and **shortest** strips in Question 2. Then write the difference in millimeters and meters.

The difference is _____ mm which is the same as _____ m.

Step Ahead ▶ The word **meter** comes from the ancient Greek word **metron**, meaning measure. The prefix **milli** comes from the Latin word for **one-thousand**.

Write another unit of measurement that involves thousandths. _____

What are some things you know about one kilometer?

Do you know what the prefix "kilo" means?

How many meters are in one kilometer? How do you know?

What are some distances that you think are about one kilometer long? How could you check?

Complete this diagram to show the length of the 5-km Fun Run in meters.

| 5 km | is the same length as | _____ m |

How many kilometers is 2,500 meters?

How would you write this as a decimal fraction or mixed number?

Show how you would write 3,725 meters as a decimal fraction and common fraction.

| _____ km | is the same length as | _____ km |

Step Up ▶ I. Write the length of these airport runways in kilometers.

a. Los Angeles (LAX)	b. St Louis (STL)	c. Chicago (ORD)	d. New York City (JFK)
3,685 m	3,359 m	3,963 m	4,423 m
_____ km	_____ km	_____ km	_____ km

2. Convert these runway lengths to meters.

a. **Seattle (SEA)** 3.627 km	b. **Dallas (DFW)** 4.085 km	c. **Washington (IAD)** 3.505 km	d. **Denver (KDEN)** 4.877 km
_____ m	_____ m	_____ m	_____ m

3. Write each length as a decimal fraction then as a mixed number.

a. **3,650 m**	b. **2,780 m**	c. **4,190 m**	d. **1,325 m**
_____ km	_____ km	_____ km	_____ km
$3\dfrac{650}{1000}$ km	km	km	km

Step Ahead

Estimate the height of each building in meters and as a decimal fraction of a kilometer.

A Burj Khalifa, Dubai

_____ m _____ km

B Taipei 101 Tower, Taiwan

_____ m _____ km

C Shanghai World Financial Center, China

_____ m _____ km

D Petronas Towers 1 and 2, Malaysia

_____ m _____ km

E Willis Tower, North America

_____ m _____ km

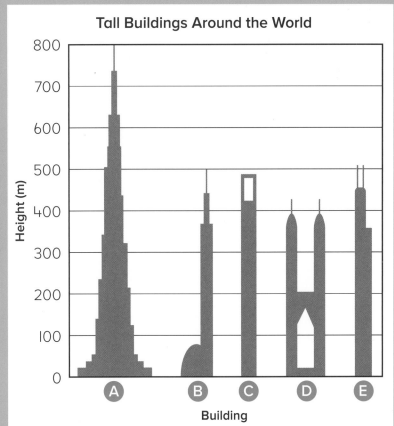

Tall Buildings Around the World

Solving Multi-Step Word Problems Involving Conversions of Metric Lengths

Evan has to fence a large rectangular field that has these dimensions. He has 5 km of fencing.

How many meters of fencing will he have left over?

What is the first step in solving this problem?

1.6 km

800 m

I would convert one dimension so I can calculate the perimeter.

Which dimension would you convert? Why?

*We can use any symbol to label the unknown value but let's call it **L** for leftover amount.*

How can you figure out the unknown value which is the amount left over?

Write a number sentence to show how you could figure out the value of L. Be sure to use the correct units.

Step Up

I. Figure out the unknown value in each problem. Show your thinking.

a. The swimming pool is 50 m long. Julia swims 30 lengths each week. How many kilometers does she swim in 4 weeks?

_____ km

b. Manuel is running a 5-km fun run. He ran 1,500 m to Checkpoint 1, then $1\frac{3}{4}$ km to Checkpoint 2. How many more meters does he have left to run?

_____ m

2. Solve each problem. Show your thinking and use a symbol to represent the unknown value.

a. Luis competed in a hop, skip, and jump event. His hop was 1.85 m. His skip was 1,720 mm. His total was 5.82 m. How long was his jump?

_____ mm

b. Claire had a 10-meter ball of string. She cut 6 lengths at 40 cm each and 5 lengths at 600 mm each. How much string did she use?

_____ cm

3. Solve each problem. Write your answer two ways. Show your thinking.

a. The perimeter of a triangle is 750 mm. The base is 23 cm long. The longest side is 400 mm long. How long is the other side?

_____ mm   _____ cm

b. Daniel drew a chart with 5 columns. Three columns were 35 mm wide and 2 were 5 cm wide. How wide was the finished chart?

_____ mm   _____ cm

Step Ahead

Write a word problem to match this equation. Then calculate the product.

250 m × 5 × 52 = [ ] _____ km

_____

_____

_____

_____

Working Space

This set of 12 eggs is one whole.

Damon needs to use $\frac{3}{4}$ of the eggs for his family's breakfast.

How many eggs are needed? How do you know?

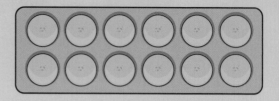

> I split the 12 eggs into 4 equal groups. Each group is $\frac{1}{4}$ of the whole. $\frac{3}{4}$ means 3 groups of $\frac{1}{4}$.

Use the diagram above to show how the eggs could have been split into 4 equal groups.

How many eggs make $\frac{3}{4}$ of 12?

Claire wrote $\frac{3}{4}$ × 12 to describe the number of eggs needed.

> $\frac{3}{4}$ × 12 means $\frac{3}{4}$ of 12.

Step Up ▶ I. Use the diagram to find each amount. Then write an equation to match.

a. $\frac{2}{3}$ of 6

$\boxed{} × \boxed{} = \boxed{}$

b. $\frac{4}{5}$ of 15

$\boxed{} × \boxed{} = \boxed{}$

c. $\frac{5}{6}$ of 18

$\boxed{} × \boxed{} = \boxed{}$

d. $\frac{3}{4}$ of 24

$\boxed{} × \boxed{} = \boxed{}$

2. Calculate each product. Show your thinking.

a. $\dfrac{2}{7} \times 21 =$	**b.** $\dfrac{5}{8} \times 32 =$
c. $\dfrac{3}{4} \times 28 =$	**d.** $\dfrac{5}{6} \times 24 =$
e. $\dfrac{3}{5} \times 45 =$	**f.** $\dfrac{2}{9} \times 63 =$

3. Use the product of the first equation to help find the product of the second equation. Show your thinking.

a.

$\dfrac{1}{3} \times 9 = \boxed{}$ ____

$\dfrac{4}{3} \times 9 = \boxed{}$ _____

b.

$\dfrac{1}{7} \times 28 = \boxed{}$ ____

$\dfrac{8}{7} \times 28 = \boxed{}$ _____

c.

$\dfrac{1}{6} \times 36 = \boxed{}$ ____

$\dfrac{9}{6} \times 36 = \boxed{}$ _____

Step Ahead Look at the two examples below. Why do you think the products will be the same? Use the diagrams to help explain.

Example 1

$\dfrac{3}{5} \times 10 = \boxed{}$

Example 2

$(\dfrac{1}{5} \times 10) \times 3 = \boxed{}$

$\boxed{} \times 3 = \boxed{}$

_____

_____

_____

_____

Multiplying Whole Numbers, Common Fractions, and Mixed Numbers

This recipe makes one batch of granola. Emma wants to make 4 batches.

How would you figure out the new amount for each ingredient?

Which ingredient matches each of these sentences?

Granola Mix

$1\frac{2}{3}$ cups oats

$\frac{2}{3}$ cup crushed almonds

$1\frac{1}{3}$ cups mixed dried fruit

$\frac{1}{2}$ cup of toasted coconut

$\frac{1}{2}$ cup buckwheat

$4 \times \frac{2}{3} =$

$4 \times 1\frac{1}{3} =$

$4 \times 1\frac{2}{3} =$

Amos used a number line and made 4 jumps of $\frac{2}{3}$ to figure out the amount of crushed almonds.

Draw jumps on this number line to show his thinking.

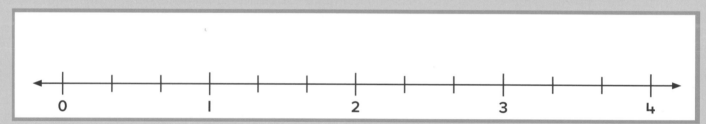

What amount of almonds is needed for 4 batches? How do you know?

When you multiply a whole number by a common fraction, what happens to the numerator? What happens to the denominator?

Carmen used the same thinking to figure out the amount of dried fruit.

She wrote this number sentence.

$$4 \times 1\frac{1}{3} = 4 \times \frac{4}{3} = \frac{16}{3}$$

Why do you think she changed $1\frac{1}{3}$ to $\frac{4}{3}$ to multiply?

What is a quick way to figure out the amount without making jumps?

Isabelle decided to calculate $4 \times 1\frac{1}{3}$ in parts.

She used this diagram to help record her thinking.

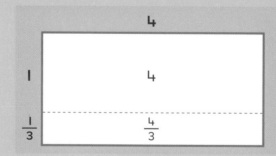

$4 \times 1\frac{1}{3}$

$(4 \times 1) + (4 \times \frac{1}{3})$

$4 + \frac{4}{3}$

$4 + 1 + \frac{1}{3} = 5\frac{1}{3}$

Look at Carmen's and Isabelle's answers. Who is correct? How do you know?

For each of these, calculate the product in two ways.

a.

$5 \times 2\frac{1}{3}$

Multiply the parts

$(5 \times \boxed{}) + (5 \times \dfrac{}{})$

$\boxed{} + \dfrac{}{} = \boxed{}$

Use improper fractions

$5 \times \dfrac{}{} = \dfrac{}{}$

b.

$3 \times 4\frac{3}{4}$

Multiply the parts

$(3 \times \boxed{}) + (3 \times \dfrac{}{})$

$\boxed{} + \dfrac{}{} = \boxed{}$

Use improper fractions

$3 \times \dfrac{}{} = \dfrac{}{}$

c.

$4 \times 2\frac{2}{5}$

Multiply the parts

$(4 \times \boxed{}) + (4 \times \dfrac{}{})$

$\boxed{} + \dfrac{}{} = \boxed{}$

Use improper fractions

$4 \times \dfrac{}{} = \dfrac{}{}$

Step Ahead This is a different granola recipe.

Toasted Granola

$1\frac{1}{2}$ cups toasted oats

$\frac{1}{3}$ cup sesame seeds

$1\frac{1}{3}$ cups mixed dried fruit

$\frac{1}{3}$ cup of sunflower seeds

1 tablespoon of honey

a. How many batches would you need to make so that all of the ingredient amounts are whole numbers? $\boxed{}$

b. Write the new amounts for each ingredient.

$\boxed{}$ cups toasted oats $\boxed{}$ cups sesame seeds

$\boxed{}$ cups mixed dried fruit $\boxed{}$ cups of sunflower seeds $\boxed{}$ tablespoons of honey

Multiplying a Proper Fraction by a Proper Fraction (Area Model)

Alex needed a pane of glass that measured $\frac{2}{3}$ yard by $\frac{3}{4}$ yard.

How could you use this diagram to calculate the area of the pane of glass?

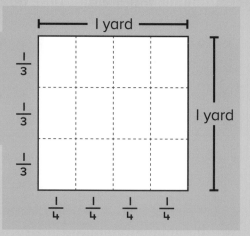

To find the area of a rectangle, I need to multiply the dimensions.

$\frac{2}{3}$ yard by $\frac{3}{4}$ yard **is the same as** $\frac{2}{3} \times \frac{3}{4} = \frac{}{}$ yd²

Alex shaded $\frac{2}{3}$ of the diagram with purple stripes and $\frac{3}{4}$ of the diagram with red stripes.

How does the diagram match the number sentence above?

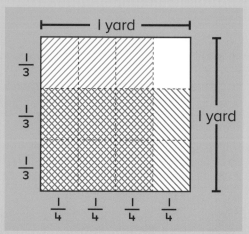

How many equal parts divide the whole square?

How many of these parts show both purple and red stripes?

What is the area of the pane of glass?

Step Up

1. Figure out the products. Use different color stripes on each array to show your thinking.

a.

$\frac{1}{3} \times \frac{1}{4} = \frac{}{}$

b.

$\frac{2}{3} \times \frac{2}{3} = \frac{}{}$

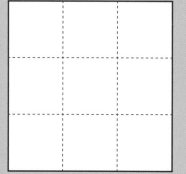

c.

$\frac{1}{4} \times \frac{1}{4} = \frac{}{}$

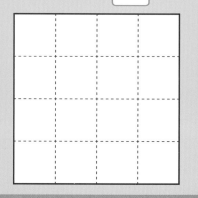

2. Draw and color an array to match each equation. Then write the product.

a.

$\frac{3}{8} \times \frac{3}{4} = \boxed{}$

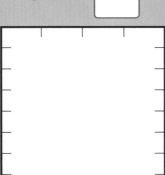

b.

$\frac{5}{8} \times \frac{2}{3} = \boxed{}$

c.

$\frac{5}{6} \times \frac{3}{4} = \boxed{}$

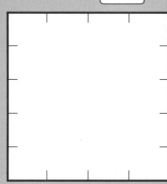

d.

$\frac{4}{5} \times \frac{3}{6} = \boxed{}$

e.

$\frac{3}{5} \times \frac{2}{3} = \boxed{}$

f.

$\frac{2}{5} \times \frac{1}{4} = \boxed{}$

Step Ahead Study the numerators and denominators in each equation in Question 2.

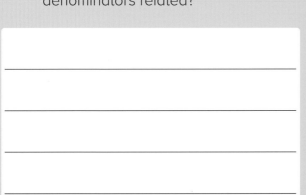

a. How are the numerators related in each equation? How are the denominators related?

b. How can you multiply these fractions without using an array picture?

$\frac{2}{5} \times \frac{3}{4} = \boxed{}$

Look at this grid.

How could you use it to show an array for this equation?

$$\frac{5}{3} \times \frac{3}{4} = \boxed{}$$

How would you figure out the product?

How would you figure out the product for each of these equations?

$$\frac{5}{3} \times \frac{5}{4} = \boxed{} \qquad \frac{5}{3} \times \frac{7}{4} = \boxed{}$$

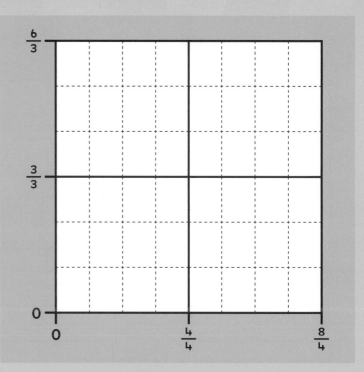

What do you notice about the numerators of the factors and the numerator of the product in each equation?

What do you notice about the denominators?

Use fractions on this grid to write an equation that has a product of I.

$$\boxed{} \times \boxed{} = 1$$

Step Up

I.   Use the grid to help you figure out the product in each equation.

a.
$$\frac{2}{3} \times \frac{2}{5} = \boxed{}$$

b.
$$\frac{4}{3} \times \frac{2}{5} = \boxed{}$$

c.
$$\frac{4}{3} \times \frac{4}{5} = \boxed{}$$

d.
$$\frac{2}{3} \times \frac{6}{5} = \boxed{}$$

e.
$$\frac{5}{3} \times \frac{7}{5} = \boxed{}$$

f.
$$\frac{6}{3} \times \frac{8}{5} = \boxed{}$$

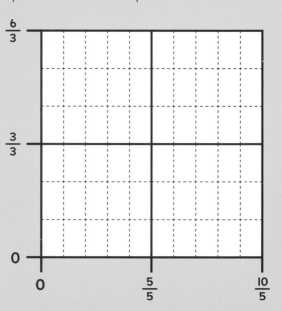

© ORIGO Education.

2. Complete each equation. Use the grid to help you.

a.
$$\frac{1}{5} \times \frac{1}{4} = \boxed{}$$

b.
$$\frac{6}{5} \times \frac{3}{4} = \boxed{}$$

c.
$$\frac{4}{5} \times \frac{5}{4} = \boxed{}$$

d.
$$\frac{3}{5} \times \frac{7}{4} = \boxed{}$$

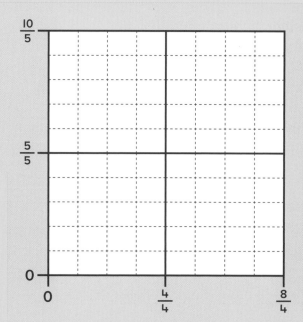

> A **proper fraction** has a numerator that is less than or equal to its denominator. An **improper fraction** has a numerator that is greater than its denominator.

3. Color the ⬭ beside the best description of each product.

a.

a **proper fraction** multiplied by a **proper fraction**

- ⬭ always less than 1
- ⬭ sometimes less than 1
- ⬭ never less than 1

b.

a **proper fraction** multiplied by an **improper fraction**

- ⬭ always less than 1
- ⬭ sometimes less than 1
- ⬭ never less than 1

c.

an **improper fraction** multiplied by an **improper fraction**

- ⬭ always less than 1
- ⬭ sometimes less than 1
- ⬭ never less than 1

Step Ahead

When the numerator and denominator of a fraction switch positions, the result is called the **reciprocal**. For example, the reciprocal of $\frac{2}{3}$ is $\frac{3}{2}$.

Draw lines to join pairs of reciprocal fractions below.

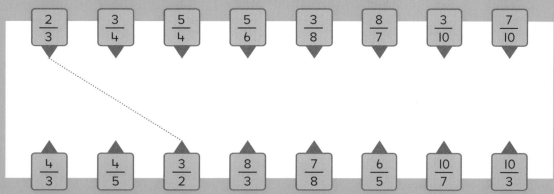

9.5 Multiplying Mixed Numbers (Area Model)

Alisa drew this grid to help her compare the area of rugs with different dimensions.

To figure out the area of a rug that measured $\frac{2}{3}$ yd by $1\frac{1}{4}$ yd, she wrote this number sentence.

$$\frac{2}{3} \times 1\frac{1}{4} = \boxed{}$$

How do you think Alisa used the grid to find the area of the rug?

How would you figure out the area of rugs with these dimensions?

$1\frac{1}{2}$ yd by $1\frac{1}{3}$ yd

$1\frac{3}{4}$ yd by $1\frac{2}{3}$ yd

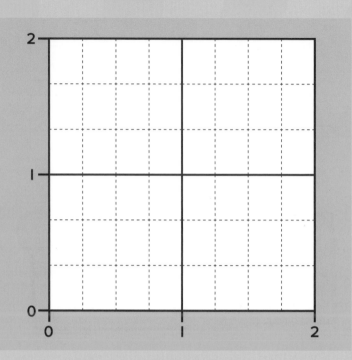

One way to multiply mixed numbers is to change them to improper fractions.

Step Up

1. Use the grid to help you figure out the product in each equation.

a. $\frac{3}{5} \times 1\frac{1}{3} = \boxed{}$

b. $1\frac{1}{5} \times 1\frac{2}{3} = \boxed{}$

c. $1\frac{2}{5} \times 2\frac{1}{3} = \boxed{}$

d. $1\frac{4}{5} \times 2\frac{2}{3} = \boxed{}$

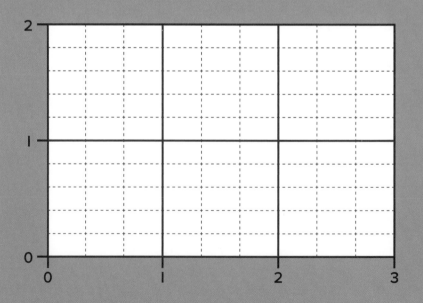

2. Complete each equation. Use the grid to help you.

a.
$$\frac{3}{5} \times 1\frac{1}{4} = \boxed{}$$

b.
$$1\frac{1}{5} \times 1\frac{1}{2} = \boxed{}$$

c.
$$1\frac{2}{5} \times 1\frac{3}{4} = \boxed{}$$

d.
$$1\frac{3}{5} \times 2\frac{3}{4} = \boxed{}$$

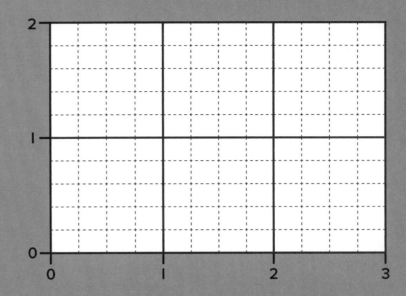

3. Convert each mixed number to an improper fraction and find the product. Write the product as an improper fraction and then as a mixed number. Then answer the question.

a.
$$1\frac{1}{2} \times 1\frac{1}{5}$$

$$\frac{\boxed{}}{2} \times \frac{\boxed{}}{5} = \frac{\boxed{}}{\boxed{}}$$

$$\boxed{}$$

How does the product compare to the product in Question 2b?

_____

_____

_____

b.
$$2\frac{3}{4} \times 1\frac{3}{5}$$

$$\frac{\boxed{}}{4} \times \frac{\boxed{}}{5} = \frac{\boxed{}}{\boxed{}}$$

$$\boxed{}$$

How does the product compare to the product in Question 2d?

_____

_____

_____

Step Ahead ▶ Use mixed numbers from the grid in Question 1 on page 208 to complete this equation so that it is true.

Some grasshoppers can jump about 3 feet.

Did you know that some kangaroos can travel about 30 feet in one jump?

So in one jump, a kangaroo can travel 10 times as far as a grasshopper.

How does this diagram show that the kangaroo's jump is 10 times as far as the grasshopper's jump?

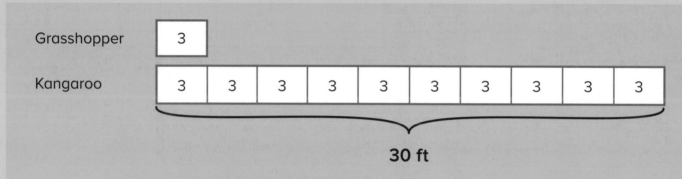

| Grasshopper | 3 |
| Kangaroo | 3 3 3 3 3 3 3 3 3 3 |

30 ft

Julia wrote this to describe the diagram.

The kangaroo's jump is 10 times longer than the grasshopper's jump.

Complete this equation to match.

$3 \times \boxed{} = 30$

Step Up   I.   Complete the sentence and equation to match each diagram.

a.

A | 2 |

B | 2 : 2 : 2 : 2 : 2 |

10 ft

Strip B is _____ times longer.

$2 \times \underline{} = 10$

b.

A | $\frac{1}{2}$ |

B | $\frac{1}{2}$: $\frac{1}{2}$: $\frac{1}{2}$: $\frac{1}{2}$: $\frac{1}{2}$: $\frac{1}{2}$ |

3 yd

Strip B is _____ times longer.

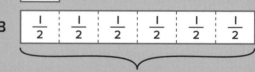
$\frac{1}{2} \times \underline{} = 3$

2. For each of these, complete the diagram to compare the amounts. Then write an equation to match.

a.

A $\frac{1}{3}$

B

2 yd

─── × □ = □

b.

A $\frac{1}{2}$

B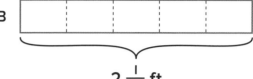

$2\frac{1}{2}$ ft

─── × □ = □

c.

A 6

B

18

□ × □ = □

d.

A $\frac{1}{4}$

B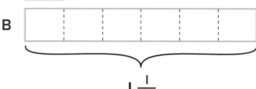

$1\frac{1}{2}$

─── × □ = □

3. Write two **whole numbers** to make each statement true. Then complete the equation to match each statement.

a.

□ cups is 6 times as much as □ cups.   □ × □ = □

b.

□ cups is 12 times as much as □ cups.   □ × □ = □

Step Ahead   Read each puzzle. Write the missing numbers.

a.

Box A holds 8 times as much as Box B.
Box B holds twice as much as Box C.

Box A holds □ times as much as Box C.

b.

Box D holds $\frac{1}{2}$ the amount of Box E.
Box E holds 4 times as much as Box F.

Box D holds □ times as much as Box F.

Exploring Multiplication by Fractions Less Than, Equal to, or Greater Than I

Carlos and Anna created a multiplication game with two number cubes.

They wrote whole numbers on one cube and fractions on the other cube. They rolled both cubes and multiplied the whole number by the fraction.

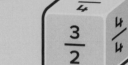

Here is the way they scored points:

> - A product greater than the whole number scores I point.
> - A product equal to the whole number scores 2 points.
> - A product less than the whole number scores 3 points.

What are some different multiplication equations Carlos and Anna could write for the numbers you can see on the cubes?

What will be the score for each of these equations?

$5 \times \dfrac{3}{4} =$ ☐ —— $4 \times \dfrac{3}{2} =$ ☐ ——

Why does the equation $6 \times \dfrac{4}{4} =$ ☐ score 2 points?

Step Up

I. For each of these, complete the equations. Then write **less than**, **equal to**, or **greater than** to complete the statement so it is true for all the equations.

a.

$7 \times \dfrac{2}{5} =$ ☐ $\dfrac{3}{4} \times \dfrac{2}{5} =$ ☐ $\dfrac{4}{3} \times \dfrac{2}{5} =$ ☐ $\dfrac{6}{6} \times \dfrac{2}{5} =$ ☐

If a number is multiplied by $\dfrac{2}{5}$, the product is _____ the number.

b.

$5 \times \dfrac{4}{3} =$ ☐ $\dfrac{5}{6} \times \dfrac{4}{3} =$ ☐ $\dfrac{6}{5} \times \dfrac{4}{3} =$ ☐ $\dfrac{8}{8} \times \dfrac{4}{3} =$ ☐

If a number is multiplied by $\dfrac{4}{3}$, the product is _____ the number.

c.

$5 \times \dfrac{3}{3} =$ ☐ $\dfrac{2}{7} \times \dfrac{3}{3} =$ ☐ $\dfrac{5}{4} \times \dfrac{3}{3} =$ ☐ $\dfrac{7}{7} \times \dfrac{3}{3} =$ ☐

If a number is multiplied by $\dfrac{3}{3}$, the product is _____ the number.

2. For each of these, color the ⬭ beside the statement that best describes the product. Then write the product.

a.

$$3 \times \frac{2}{5} = \frac{}{}$$

○ The product is greater than the first factor.
○ The product is equal to the first factor.
○ The product is less than the first factor.

b.

$$\frac{4}{3} \times \frac{7}{5} = \frac{}{}$$

○ The product is greater than the first factor.
○ The product is equal to the first factor.
○ The product is less than the first factor.

c.

$$\frac{2}{3} \times \frac{5}{5} = \frac{}{}$$

○ The product is greater than the first factor.
○ The product is equal to the first factor.
○ The product is less than the first factor.

d.

$$7 \times \frac{6}{5} = \frac{}{}$$

○ The product is greater than the first factor.
○ The product is equal to the first factor.
○ The product is less than the first factor.

3. Write **different fractions** to complete the equations to match the statement.

a. The product is **equal to** the first factor.

$$\frac{7}{4} \times \boxed{} = \boxed{}$$

$$1\frac{2}{3} \times \boxed{} = \boxed{}$$

b. The product is **greater than** the first factor.

$$\frac{3}{8} \times \boxed{} = \boxed{}$$

$$1\frac{3}{4} \times \boxed{} = \boxed{}$$

c. The product is **less than** the first factor.

$$\frac{8}{5} \times \boxed{} = \boxed{}$$

$$1\frac{2}{5} \times \boxed{} = \boxed{}$$

Step Ahead

Imagine Carlos and Anna replaced the whole-number cube below with one showing $\frac{1}{6}$, $\frac{2}{6}$, $\frac{3}{6}$, $\frac{4}{6}$, $\frac{5}{6}$, and $\frac{6}{6}$.

a. What rolls would give a product that is **equal to** both of the factors?

b. What rolls would give a product that is **less than** both of the factors?

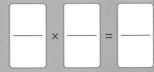

Solving Word Problems Involving Mixed Numbers

This recipe makes one large bowl of punch.

Brady wants to make three of these large bowls.

How could you figure out the total amount of each ingredient that he will need?

He is making 3 bowls of punch, so that is like multiplying by 3.

Fruit Punch

$\frac{3}{4}$ cup apple juice

$\frac{3}{4}$ cup water

$2\frac{1}{4}$ cups orange juice

$1\frac{1}{2}$ cups pineapple juice

2 cups of iced tea

How much of each ingredient will Brady need?

Dakota decides to use $1\frac{1}{2}$ times the recipe to make extra punch.
He wrote this equation to figure out the amount of apple juice.

Why did he change $1\frac{1}{2}$ to $\frac{3}{2}$ to multiply?

$$\frac{3}{4} \times \frac{3}{2} = \boxed{}$$

What equations would you write to figure out the other ingredient amounts he will need?

How much will he need of each ingredient to make $1\frac{1}{2}$ times the recipe?

Step Up

1. Figure out each length. Show your thinking. You can draw a picture to help.

a. Carter needs 6 lengths of ribbon to make bows for a party. Each ribbon is $1\frac{3}{4}$ yd long. What is the total length of the ribbon he needs to buy?

_____ yd

b. Akari is making a square picture frame. The length of a side is $2\frac{2}{3}$ ft. What is the total length of the wood she needs?

_____ ft

2. Solve each problem. Show your thinking.

a. Aran works $1\frac{3}{4}$ hours each day at his part-time job. He is paid $6 each hour. How much does he earn in one day?

$ _____

b. Maka is covering the top of a table with tiles. The table measures $2\frac{1}{4}$ ft by $3\frac{1}{3}$ ft. The tiles cost $3 a square foot. What is the area of the table top and what is the cost of the tiles?

Area _____ sq ft   Total cost $ _____

c. Ashley needs to buy sod to cover a rectangular shaped section of her yard. The section measures $4\frac{1}{2}$ yd by $5\frac{1}{4}$ yd. The sod costs $8 a square yard. What is the area of the section and the total cost of the sod?

Area _____ sq yd   Total cost $ _____

Step Ahead

A small table measures $2\frac{3}{4}$ ft by $3\frac{2}{3}$ ft. The dimensions of a large table are exactly double those of the small table. How many times greater is the area of the large table top than the small table top?

_____

$3\frac{2}{3}$ ft

$2\frac{3}{4}$ ft   **Small Table**

Working Space

Solving Multi-Step Word Problems Involving Fractions and Mixed Numbers

Eva works at a framing store.
She works with fractions and mixed numbers in many different ways.

This diagram shows the dimensions of a mirror that she needs to frame.

How would you figure out the total length of wood needed to build the frame?

What equation would you write? How did you decide?

What is the total length?

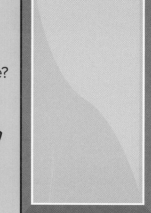

$1\frac{1}{4}$ ft

$2\frac{2}{3}$ ft

> Remember that mixed numbers can be changed to improper fractions.

Eva decides to allow one extra inch at each end of each side of the frame for any errors that she might make.
How would you figure out the total length of wood she now requires?

What equation would you write? How did you decide?

What is the total length?

> Remember to work with the same units. One inch is $\frac{1}{12}$ of a foot.

Eva has a strip of wood that is $8\frac{1}{2}$ feet long. Will this strip be long enough to make the frame?

What is the area of the mirror including the frame?

Step Up

1. Amber has a mirror that is one foot longer and one foot wider than the frame pictured above. Solve these problems about Amber's mirror. Show the thinking you use. You can draw a picture to help.

a. What is the perimeter of Amber's mirror?

_____ ft

b. What is the area of Amber's mirror including the frame?

_____ ft²

2. Solve each problem. Show your thinking.

a. Imagine a mirror that is $\frac{1}{4}$ foot wider and $\frac{1}{3}$ foot shorter than the mirror pictured at the top of page 216. What is the perimeter of the new mirror?

_____ ft

b. This picture shows the outside dimensions of a frame. The width of the frame is $\frac{1}{4}$ ft. What is the area of the picture **inside** the frame?

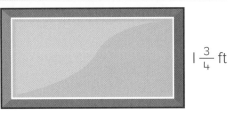

$1\frac{3}{4}$ ft

$2\frac{1}{2}$ ft

_____ ft²

c. This picture is to be framed. The width of the wood used for the frame will be $\frac{1}{3}$ ft. What will be the **outside** perimeter of the frame?

$1\frac{1}{2}$ ft

$2\frac{1}{3}$ ft

_____ ft

Step Ahead Draw and label the dimensions of a frame you could make from a strip of wood that is $12\frac{1}{2}$ ft long.

What is the weight of each package?

How could you figure out the difference in weight between these two packages?

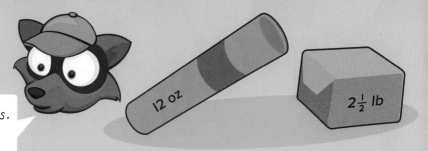

> I would convert the pounds into ounces. I know there are 16 oz in 1 pound.

12 oz

$2\frac{1}{2}$ lb

How could you figure out the number of ounces in one-half of a pound?

Complete these statements.

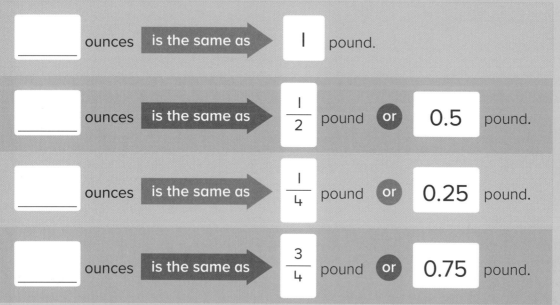

_____ ounces is the same as **1** pound.

_____ ounces is the same as $\frac{1}{2}$ pound **or** **0.5** pound.

_____ ounces is the same as $\frac{1}{4}$ pound **or** **0.25** pound.

_____ ounces is the same as $\frac{3}{4}$ pound **or** **0.75** pound.

What are some other statements you could write?

> I wonder how many ounces are in $\frac{1}{8}$ of a pound?

Step Up

1. Convert ounces to pounds to complete these.

a. 20 oz = _____ lb _____ oz

b. 26 oz = _____ lb _____ oz

c. 33 oz = _____ lb _____ oz

d. 22 oz = _____ lb _____ oz

e. 18 oz = _____ lb _____ oz

f. 39 oz = _____ lb _____ oz

2. Convert pounds to ounces to complete these. Show your thinking.

a.

3.5 lb = _____ oz

b.

2.75 lb = _____ oz

c.

4.25 lb = _____ oz

d.

5.5 lb = _____ oz

e.

10.75 lb = _____ oz

f.

6.25 lb = _____ oz

3. Write the missing mass to make each balance picture true.

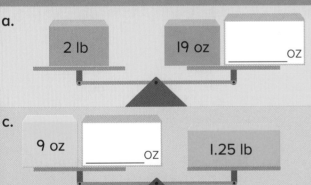

a.

2 lb   19 oz   _____ oz

b.

10 oz   _____ oz   1.5 lb

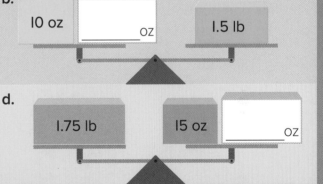

c.

9 oz   _____ oz   1.25 lb

d.

1.75 lb   15 oz   _____ oz

Step Ahead

The total mass of these items is 3.25 lb. One item is 2 lb. Write a possible mass for each other item.

Working Space

_____ oz

_____ oz

_____ oz

2 lb

Solving Word Problems Involving Conversions Between Units of Mass

Kayla buys these grocery items.

What is the heaviest item she buys? How do you know?

At the checkout, the tuna cans and crackers are packed into one bag. What is the total mass of this bag? Does it weigh more or less than 2 lb?

> The 3 cans of tuna weigh 12 oz each. The crackers weigh 8 oz. I will call the total mass **M**. M = 3 × 12 + 8

The carrots and potatoes are packed together in another bag. What is the total mass of this bag?

Is the bag with potatoes and carrots heavier or lighter than the box of laundry powder?

Step Up

I. Refer to the grocery items above to solve each problem. Show your thinking.

a. If the tuna cans and potatoes were packed together in one bag, what would be the total mass of this bag?

_____ OZ

b. The laundry powder is packed with one other item. The total mass of this bag is $5\frac{1}{2}$ lb. What is the other item in the bag?

_____

2. Solve these word problems. Show your thinking.

a. A 2-lb block of cheese is cut into 8 pieces of equal mass. What is the mass of each piece?

_____ oz

b. Deon buys 1.5 lb of turkey and 10 oz of grilled capsicum. What is the total mass of his purchase?

_____ oz

c. Zola has 4 lb of flour. She needs to use 12 oz of flour for a quiche she is baking. How much flour will be left?

_____ oz

d. Half a pound of butter is needed to make one batch of muffins. How many batches of muffins can be made from 45 oz?

_____ batches

Step Ahead Figure out a fair price for the large packet of spaghetti. Then write why you think it is fair.

$ _____

SPAGHETTI
2 lb

98¢

SPAGHETTI
8 oz

Interpreting Line Plots to Solve Real-World Problems (Involving Ounces)

Nadie bakes and sells loaves of homemade bread.
With the recipe she uses, each loaf should weigh 22 oz.

Some loaves seem larger than others so she decides to investigate.

What could she do? How could she carry out the investigation?

She decides to weigh each of the loaves that she made that day.

The line plot below shows the mass of each loaf.

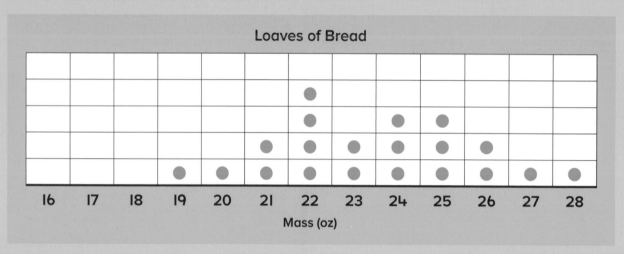

Loaves of Bread

Mass (oz)

What do you notice?

What does the shape of the line plot tell you about the loaves of bread?

More than half of the loaves weigh more than 22 oz.

Why did she use a line plot to show her findings?

What could she do with the findings?
What changes could she make to the recipe or selling price?

Imagine you randomly selected one loaf of bread.

What do you think it would weigh? Explain your thinking.

Jack bakes and sells banana bread. Each loaf of banana bread should weigh 30 oz. The line plot below shows the mass of 20 loaves.

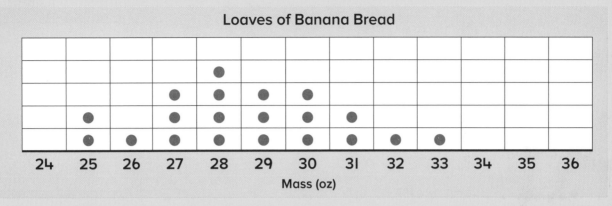

Loaves of Banana Bread

Mass (oz)

a. What does the shape of the line plot tell you about the loaves of bread?

b. Imagine you randomly selected one loaf of banana bread. What do you think it would weigh? Explain your thinking.

The information below was collected at an animal reserve. Lion cubs typically gain about 25 oz in their first week.

What concerns might the reserve managers have? Explain why.

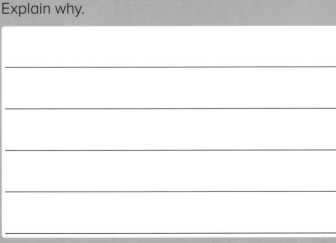

Weight Gained by Newborn Lion Cubs in First Week

Ounces

© ORIGO Education.

This large square represents one whole.
What fraction is shaded? How do you know?

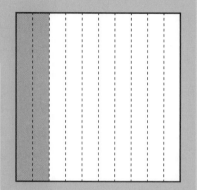

How would you write the fraction that is shaded?

Two-tenths of the whole square is shaded so that's $\frac{2}{10}$ or 0.2.

The shaded part shows one group of 0.2. How could you show 4 groups of 0.2?

Nina used this number line to show the multiplication another way.

What jumps did she make? How will it help her figure out the product?

Draw more jumps on the number line to figure out 6 × 0.2.

What decimal fraction would you write to show the product?

Step Up   1.   Write the products. Color or outline parts of the squares to show your thinking.

a.

3 × 0.2 = _____

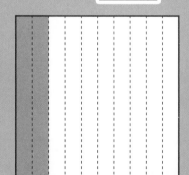

b.

2 × 0.4 = _____

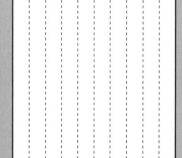

c.

3 × 0.3 = _____

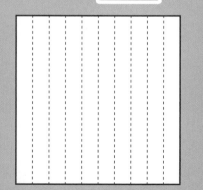

2. Complete each equation. Draw jumps on the number line to show your thinking.

a.

$4 \times 0.3 =$ _____

0   1   2

b.

$7 \times 0.2 =$ _____

0   1   2

c.

$3 \times 0.4 =$ _____

0   1   2

d.

$5 \times 0.2 =$ _____

0   1   2

e.

$3 \times 0.5 =$ _____

0   1   2

f.

$4 \times 0.4 =$ _____

0   1   2

Step Ahead Complete each equation. Describe a pattern you see.

a.
$7 \times 4 =$ _____
$7 \times 0.4 =$ _____

b.
$9 \times 5 =$ _____
$9 \times 0.5 =$ _____

c.
$6 \times 3 =$ _____
$6 \times 0.3 =$ _____

d.
$8 \times 9 =$ _____
$8 \times 0.9 =$ _____

_____

_____

Using a Partial-Products Strategy to Multiply Decimal Fractions (Tenths)

This picture shows the dimensions of a room.

How could you figure out its area?

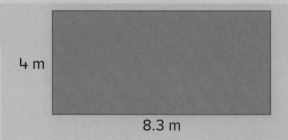

4 m

8.3 m

It must be about 32 m² because 4 × 8 = 32.

Janice split the rectangle into parts that are easier to multiply.

How did she split the rectangle?

How will it help her figure out the area?

What is the total area? How do you know?

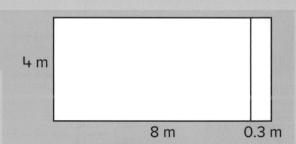

4 m

8 m   0.3 m

I figured out 4 × 8 then 4 × 0.3.
Then I added the two partial products.
That's 32 + 1.2 which is 33.2.

How would you use this strategy to figure out 4 × 2.6?

Step Up

1. Multiply the ones and then the tenths to figure out each partial product. Then write the total.

a.

buy 8 boxes   3.1 kg

(_8_ × _3_) + (_8_ × _0.1_)

_____ + _____ = _____ kg

b.

buy 7 boxes   3.2 kg

(____ × ____) + (____ × ____)

_____ + _____ = _____ kg

c.

buy 6 boxes   7.2 kg

(____ × ____) + (____ × ____)

_____ + _____ = _____ kg

d.

buy 5 boxes   8.3 kg

(____ × ____) + (____ × ____)

_____ + _____ = _____ kg

2. Multiply the parts to figure out the total weight for each purchase.

a.

buy 5 bags   **7.3 kg**

(_____ × _____) + (_____ × _____)

_____ + _____ = _____ kg

b.

buy 9 bags   **4.2 kg**

(_____ × _____) + (_____ × _____)

_____ + _____ = _____ kg

c.

buy 7 bags   **4.8 kg**

(_____ × _____) + (_____ × _____)

_____ + _____ = _____ kg

d.

buy 6 bags   **3.9 kg**

(_____ × _____) + (_____ × _____)

_____ + _____ = _____ kg

3. Complete each sentence.

a.

$6.4 × 3 =$ (_____ × _____) + (_____ × _____) = _____ + _____ = _____

b.

$3.8 × 3 =$ (_____ × _____) + (_____ × _____) = _____ + _____ = _____

4. Use the strategy from Question 2 to figure out each of these.

a. $5.6 × 4 =$ _____

b. $2.4 × 15 =$ _____

c. $3.4 × 12 =$ _____

Step Ahead

Juan moved 8 tables and 8 chairs from the classroom.
Each table weighed 7.8 kg and each chair weighed 3.2 kg.
What was the total mass of all the furniture he moved?

_____ kg

Working Space

This large square represents one whole.

What fraction is shaded? How do you know?

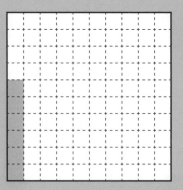

How would you write the fraction that is shaded?

Six-hundredths of the whole square is shaded so that's $\frac{6}{100}$ or 0.06.

The shaded part shows one group of 0.06. How could you show 4 groups of 0.06?

Draw jumps on this number line to show the multiplication another way.

What decimal fraction would you write to show the product?

Use the number line above to figure out 7 × 0.05.

What is the product? How do you know?

What is another way you could figure out the product?

Step Up   I.   Write the products. Color or outline parts of the squares to show your thinking.

a.
4 × 0.03 = _____

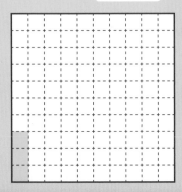

b.
3 × 0.06 = _____

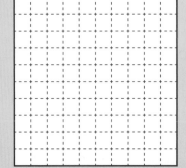

c.
9 × 0.05 = _____

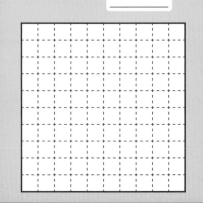

2. Complete these equations. Draw jumps on the number line to show your thinking.

a.

$5 \times 0.05 =$ ⬚

0   0.50

b.

$3 \times 0.07 =$ ⬚

0   0.50

c.

$5 \times 0.06 =$ ⬚

0   0.50

d.

$3 \times 0.09 =$ ⬚

0   0.50

3. Complete these equations.

a.

$3 \times 4 =$ _____

$3 \times 0.4 =$ _____

$3 \times 0.04 =$ _____

b.

$8 \times 3 =$ _____

$8 \times 0.3 =$ _____

$8 \times 0.03 =$ _____

c.

$9 \times 7 =$ _____

$9 \times 0.7 =$ _____

$9 \times 0.07 =$ _____

4. Look at the equations in Question 3. Describe a pattern you see.

_____

_____

Step Ahead Lilly knows $6 \times 8 = 48$. How could she use this fact to figure out 6×0.08?

_____

_____

© ORIGO Education.

This large square represents one whole.
What fraction is shaded? How do you know?

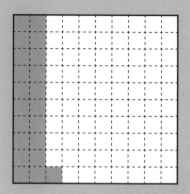

Write the fraction two different ways.

◻/100   0.◻◻◻

How could you figure out 4 × 0.21?

I would shade 4 groups of 21 hundredths.

I know 4 × 21 is 84.
0.21 is one-hundredth of 21.
So the answer must be one-hundredth of 84.

How could you figure out 6 × 0.24?

Would the product be more or less than one whole?
How do you know?

6 × 0.24 = ◻

Damon followed these steps to figure it out.

6 × 0.2 = **1.2**

Write the answer.
What steps did he follow?

6 × 0.04 = **0.24**

How could you use Damon's strategy to figure out 5 × 0.35?

Step Up   1.   Write the products. You can shade parts of each square to help your thinking.

a.
4 × 0.12 = _____

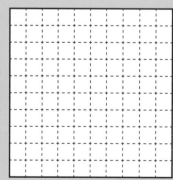

b.
5 × 0.16 = _____

c.
4 × 0.25 = _____

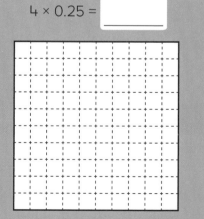

2. Figure out each partial product. Then write the total.

a.

$3 \times 0.23 =$ ☐

$3 \times 0.2 =$ ☐

$3 \times 0.03 =$ ☐

b.

$5 \times 0.15 =$ ☐

$5 \times 0.1 =$ ☐

$5 \times 0.05 =$ ☐

c.

$3 \times 0.19 =$ ☐

$3 \times 0.1 =$ ☐

$3 \times 0.09 =$ ☐

3. Figure out each product. Write number sentences to show your thinking.

a.

$5 \times 0.37 =$ _____

b.

$4 \times 0.42 =$ _____

c.

$3 \times 0.49 =$ _____

d.

$4 \times 0.38 =$ _____

e.

$3 \times 0.72 =$ _____

f.

$5 \times 0.45 =$ _____

Step Ahead

Look at this calculation. Describe the mistake in words.
Then write the correct product below.

$5 \times 0.39 = 0.60$

$5 \times 0.3 = 0.15$

$5 \times 0.09 = 0.45$

_____

_____

_____

☐ _____

Multiplying Whole Numbers and Decimal Fractions (Hundredths)

This diagram shows the area of a courtyard that has to be paved.

How could you figure out the number of square meters that will be covered?

2 m

8.25 m

I would split 8.25 into two parts.
2 x 8.25 is the same as (2 x 8) + (2 x 0.25).

0.25 is one-fourth, and 2 one-fourths is one-half.

A small box of pavers costs $6.30.

How could you estimate the total cost of 5 boxes? How do you know?

What numbers did you split to figure it out?

Step Up

I. Multiply the ones then the hundredths. Add the partial products to figure out the total cost of each purchase.

a.
buy 4 boxes   **$6.20**

(_4_ × _6_) + (_4_ × _0.20_)

_____ + _____ = $_____

b.
buy 3 boxes   **$7.15**

(___ × ___) + (___ × _____)

_____ + _____ = $_____

c.
buy 6 boxes   **$5.25**

(___ × ___) + (___ × _____)

_____ + _____ = $_____

d.
buy 5 boxes   **$8.40**

(___ × ___) + (___ × _____)

_____ + _____ = $_____

2. Figure out each partial product. Then write the total.

a.

6 × 5.12

(_____ × _____) + (_____ × _____)

_____ + _____ = _____

b.

8 × 3.25

(_____ × _____) + (_____ × _____)

_____ + _____ = _____

c.

5 × 4.09

(_____ × _____) + (_____ × _____)

_____ + _____ = _____

d.

4 × 7.35

(_____ × _____) + (_____ × _____)

_____ + _____ = _____

3. Estimate the products then complete each equation. Show your thinking.

a.

Estimate _____

3 × 5.75 = _____

b.

Estimate _____

9 × 4.20 = _____

c.

Estimate _____

6 × 8.35 = _____

Step Ahead

Mr. Martinez is tiling his bathroom. He buys 3 boxes of large tiles and 5 boxes of small tiles. What is the total cost of the tiles?

Small tiles
$5.20

Large tiles
$7.90

$ _____

Estimate the dimensions of this poster with your hands.

Do you think the area of the poster is more
or less than one square meter? Explain your thinking.

How could you figure out the exact area?
What equivalent expression could you write?

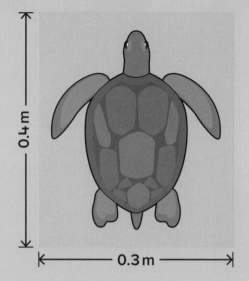

*I would use common fractions
and think $\frac{4}{10} \times \frac{3}{10}$.*

**This is a picture of a larger square that has an area
of one square meter.**

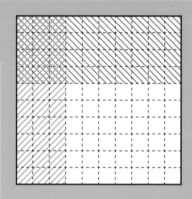

Sofia shaded parts of the square to match
the dimensions of the turtle poster above.

How do the dimensions of the poster match
the section that has two colors?

What is the area of the poster? How do you know?

Step Up   I.   Shade the square to match each expression. Then write the products.

a.
$0.4 \times 0.2 =$ _____

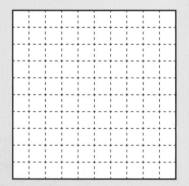

b.
$0.2 \times 0.3 =$ _____

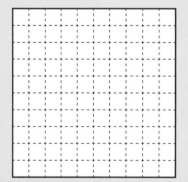

c.
$0.9 \times 0.1 =$ _____

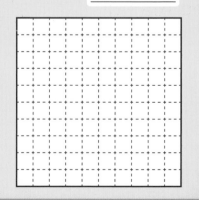

2. Write the products. Shade parts of the squares to match.

a.
0.5 × 0.3 = _____

b.
0.4 × 0.5 = _____

c.
0.6 × 0.8 = _____

d.
0.9 × 0.2 = _____

e.
0.7 × 0.8 = _____

f.
0.6 × 0.3 = _____

3. Complete each equation.

a.
0.4 × 0.8 = _____

b.
_____ × 0.5 = 0.35

c.
0.32 = _____ × 0.8

d.
_____ × 0.9 = 0.45

e.
0.06 = 0.6 × _____

f.
_____ × 0.8 = 0.72

Step Ahead

Imagine you take one ball from each jar.
Use these digits to complete
this expression.

0._____ × 0._____

_____

Is it possible to make one whole? _____

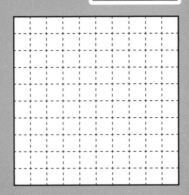

9
6 8 4
3 5 2
1 0 7

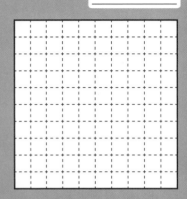

9
6 8 4
3 5 2
1 0 7

Calculate the product.

What happens when you multiply tenths by tenths?
What do you notice about the product?

$0.4 \times 0.2 =$ _____

Think about this equation.

$0.4 \times 0.02 =$ _____

Will the product be greater than or
less than 0.4×0.2? Explain your thinking.

Look at this table. What place-value patterns do you see?

	O	t	h	th
$4 \times 2 =$	8 .			
$4 \times 0.2 =$	0 .	8		
$0.4 \times 0.2 =$	0 .	0	8	
$0.4 \times 0.02 =$	.			

Continue the pattern to figure out 0.4×0.02.

How could you figure out 0.3×0.04?

Complete this equation to figure out the product.

$$\frac{}{10} \times \frac{}{100} = \frac{}{1000}$$

Tenths x tenths = hundredths.
Tenths x hundredths = thousandths.

Step Up

1. Write the common fractions that you could multiply to figure out each product.
   Then complete the equations.

a.
$0.4 \times 0.02 =$ _____

$$\frac{4}{10} \times \frac{2}{100} = \frac{8}{1000}$$

b.
$0.3 \times 0.03 =$ _____

$$\frac{}{} \times \frac{}{} = \frac{}{}$$

c.
$0.1 \times 0.07 =$ _____

$$\frac{}{} \times \frac{}{} = \frac{}{}$$

d.
$0.5 \times 0.02 =$ _____

$$\frac{}{} \times \frac{}{} = \frac{}{}$$

2. Write the common fractions that you could multiply to figure out each product. Then complete the equations.

a.

$0.7 \times 0.05 =$ _____

$\dfrac{}{} \times \dfrac{}{} = \dfrac{}{}$

b.

$0.4 \times 0.09 =$ _____

$\dfrac{}{} \times \dfrac{}{} = \dfrac{}{}$

c.

$0.8 \times 0.03 =$ _____

$\dfrac{}{} \times \dfrac{}{} = \dfrac{}{}$

d.

$0.6 \times 0.07 =$ _____

$\dfrac{}{} \times \dfrac{}{} = \dfrac{}{}$

e.

$0.5 \times 0.08 =$ _____

$\dfrac{}{} \times \dfrac{}{} = \dfrac{}{}$

f.

$0.1 \times 0.02 =$ _____

$\dfrac{}{} \times \dfrac{}{} = \dfrac{}{}$

3. Complete each equation.

a.

$0.4 \times 0.05 =$ _____

b.

$0.5 \times 0.06 =$ _____

c.

$0.8 \times 0.06 =$ _____

d.

$0.9 \times 0.02 =$ _____

e.

$0.7 \times 0.03 =$ _____

f.

$0.9 \times 0.09 =$ _____

Step Ahead   Look at these calculations. Write the correct product beside each mistake.

a. $0.4 \times 0.02 = 0.08$	**b.** $0.03 \times 0.5 = 0.015$
c. $0.9 \times 0.5 = 4.5$	**d.** $0.6 \times 0.6 = 0.34$
e. $0.5 \times 0.5 = 0.25$	**f.** $0.06 \times 0.3 = 0.18$

Imagine you need to find the area of a floor with these dimensions. What do you know about the answer?

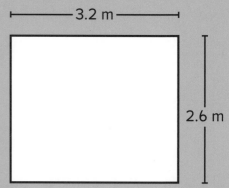

3.2 m

2.6 m

The length is a little more than 3 m and the width is a little less than 3 m so the area will be close to 9 m².

The answer will include hundredths.

How could you figure out the exact answer?

James split the rectangle into parts that were easier to multiply.

How did he split the rectangle?

How do the parts make it easier to multiply?

What partial products does he add to figure out the area?

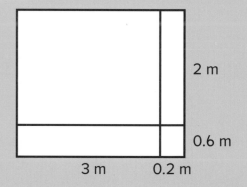

2 m

0.6 m

3 m   0.2 m

Use the same thinking to calculate the area of a room measuring **4.5 m × 2.8 m**.

Step Up Use this apartment floor plan to answer the questions on page 239.

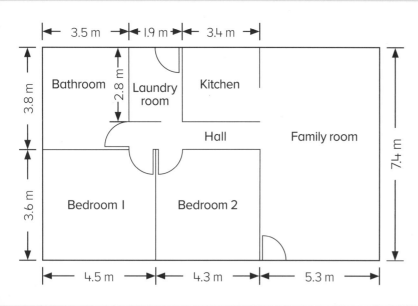

Estimate then calculate the area of each room on the plan on page 238.

a.	Bedroom I

Estimate _____ m²

_____ m²

b.	Kitchen

Estimate _____ m²

_____ m²

c.	Bathroom

Estimate _____ m²

_____ m²

d.	Bedroom 2

Estimate _____ m²

_____ m²

e.	Family room

Estimate _____ m²

_____ m²

f.	Laundry room

Estimate _____ m²

_____ m²

Step Ahead Calculate the area of the whole apartment on page 238.

_____ m²

Reinforcing the Partial-Products Strategy for Multiplication (Tenths and Hundredths)

What do you know about the area of this rectangle?

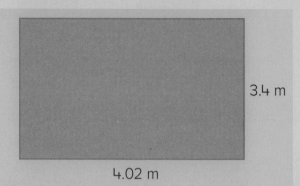

3.4 m

4.02 m

The area will be close to 12 square meters because 3 x 4 = 12.

How could you figure out the exact area?

Redraw the rectangle and split it into parts to help. Write the dimensions to show your thinking.

What partial products will you add to figure out the total area? What is the area of the rectangle?

Working Space

Remember... tenths x tenths = hundredths. Tenths x hundredths = thousandths.

Step Up

1. Draw lines to split each rectangle into parts that are easier to multiply. Figure out the partial products. Then write the total.

a.

1.02 × 3.4 = _____

b.

2.03 × 4.6 = _____

2. Complete each equation. Show the steps you use.

a.

$2.7 \times 1.05 =$ _____

b.

$4.2 \times 3.07 =$ _____

c.

$3.09 \times 3.4 =$ _____

d.

$5.1 \times 3.25 =$ _____

Step Ahead

Emily wrote partial products to figure out the area of this room.
Check her calculations and correct any mistakes. Then write the area.

$4.5 \times 5.08 =$ _____

$4 \times 5 = 20$

$4 \times 0.08 = 0.32$

$0.5 \times 5 = 2.5$

$0.5 \times 0.08 = 0.40$

4.5 m

5.08 m

How could you label the marks on this scale?

Could your label be written in more than one way?
How do you know?

The marks between 0 kg and 1 kg can be a number of grams or a fraction of a kilogram.

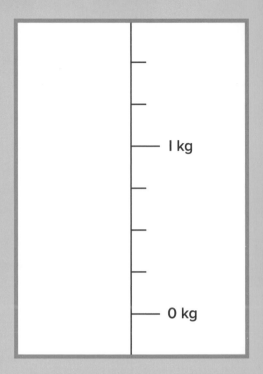

1 kg

0 kg

Label each mark in grams on the left of the scale.
What would you write to label each mark in kilograms
on the right of the scale? You can use decimal fractions
or common fractions.

How did you figure out the equivalent amounts?

Step Up   1.   Color the three ways you could write the amount shown on the scale.

a.

$2\frac{1}{2}$ kg   250 g

2,500 g   2.5 kg

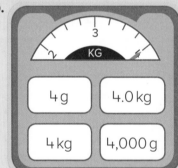

b.

4 g   4.0 kg

4 kg   4,000 g

c.

0.5 kg $\frac{1}{2}$ kg

50 g   500 g

d.

$1\frac{1}{2}$ kg $1\frac{1}{4}$ kg

1,250 g   1.25 kg

e.

750 g $\frac{3}{4}$ kg

34 g   0.75 kg

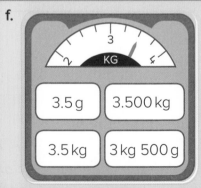

f.

3.5 g   3.500 kg

3.5 kg   3 kg 500 g

2. Draw a red needle to show the mass on the scale. Then write the mass two other ways.

a.

1.6 kg

b.

1,300 g

c.

2 kg 100 g

d.

2.2 kg

e.

$3\frac{4}{5}$ kg

f.

2,400 g

g.

1,150 g

h.

2 kg 600 g

i.

0.2 kg

Step Ahead   Rewrite these masses in order from **least** to **greatest**.

a.

| 8.1 kg | 81 g | 8.15 kg | 810 g | 8,000 g |

b.

| 3.75 kg | 375 g | 0.370 kg | 3,705 g | 37.5 kg |

Solving Multi-Step Word Problems Involving Conversions of Metric Masses

Kylie has different boxes to pack.
The boxes come in these three sizes.

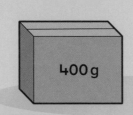

Kylie packed four of the heaviest boxes together.
What was the total mass of the package?

She then packed together two boxes of each size.
What is the total mass of this package?

> I will call the total mass **T**.
> T = 2 × (400 + 200 + 150)

What is the total mass in grams? How could you write the total mass in kilograms?

Kylie was asked to make some different
packages that each weighed exactly 2 kg.

What combinations of the boxes could she use?

How did you figure out each combination?

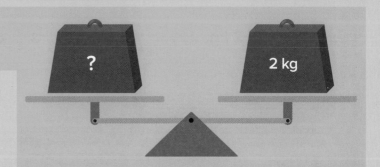

Step Up

I. Use the boxes at the top of the page to solve each word problem.

a. Kana packed seven 200-g boxes and five 150-g boxes together. What was the total mass of the package?

_____ kg

b. Three packages are each filled with 400-g boxes. Each package weighs 2 kg. How many 400-g boxes were used?

_____ boxes

2. Solve these word problems. Show your thinking.

a. A box of pasta weighs exactly one kilogram. Each small packet of pasta inside the box weighs 50 grams. How many packets of pasta are in two boxes?

_____ packets

b. A box is filled with 400-g packets of noodles. The box weighs 6 kg in total. Three packets are removed from the box. How much does the box weigh now?

_____ kg

c. There are 5 boxes of flour in a stack. Each box contains 8 packets of flour. Each packet of flour weighs 300 g. What is the total mass of flour in the stack?

_____ kg

d. A customer ordered 8 bags of rice that each weighed $\frac{1}{2}$ kg and 12 packets of popcorn that each weighed 150 g. What was the total mass of their order?

_____ kg

Step Ahead   Write a mass in each box so that the balance pictures are true.

a.

1.5 kg   _____ g   _____ g   0.9 kg

b.

750 g   _____ kg   500 g   _____ kg

Constructing and Interpreting a Line Plot (Involving Kilograms)

A farmer weighed some of his pumpkin crop.

The mass of each pumpkin was rounded to the nearest one-half of a kilogram.
This line plot shows the mass of the pumpkins.

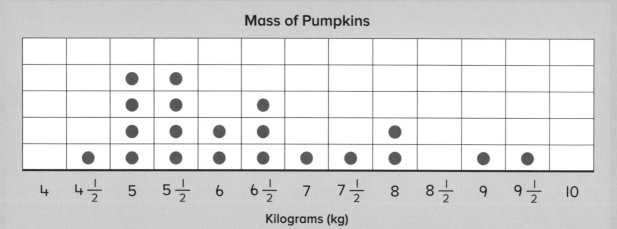

Mass of Pumpkins

Kilograms (kg)

What do you notice about the line plot?

How many pumpkins did the farmer weigh?

What is the difference in mass between the lightest and heaviest pumpkins?

How many pumpkins are heavier than $6\frac{1}{2}$ kg?

How many pumpkins are lighter than 7 kg?

The pumpkins in last season's crop weighed about $5\frac{1}{2}$ kg each.

Are the pumpkins in this season's crop
heavier or lighter? How do you know?

Step Up Another farmer weighed 20 pumpkins. Each mass is recorded below. Use this data for the line plot on page 247. You will need to convert the grams to kilograms.

6 kg	$9\frac{1}{2}$ kg	5 kg	5 kg	6,500 g
5,500 g	4 kg	$5\frac{1}{2}$ kg	$9\frac{1}{2}$ kg	7 kg
$4\frac{1}{2}$ kg	8 kg	5,000 g	$6\frac{1}{2}$ kg	$5\frac{1}{2}$ kg
4,500 g	9,000 g	$5\frac{1}{2}$ kg	$4\frac{1}{2}$ kg	$5\frac{1}{2}$ kg

I. Draw ● to represent each mass shown at the bottom of page 246.

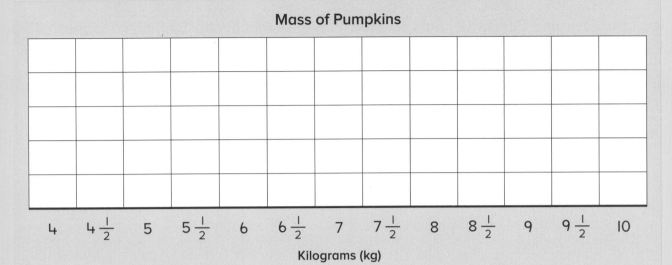

Mass of Pumpkins

Kilograms (kg)

4 4½ 5 5½ 6 6½ 7 7½ 8 8½ 9 9½ 10

2. Look at the line plot above.

   a. Which mass was recorded most often? ☐ kg

   b. How many pumpkins weighed **exactly** 6½ kg? ☐ ____

   c. How many pumpkins were **heavier** than 5 kg? ☐ ____

   d. What is the difference in mass between the lightest and heaviest pumpkins? ☐ kg

3. Imagine you randomly selected one pumpkin from Question I.
What do you think it would weigh? Explain your thinking.

_____

_____

_____

Step Ahead Compare the line plots on pages 246 and 247. Which line plot shows the heavier crop of pumpkins? Explain your thinking.

_____

_____

Relating Fractions to Division

Jack, Lela, Jose, and Mary order three square pizzas to share equally. Each friend suggested a different way to split the pizzas. The colors in their diagrams show each person's share.

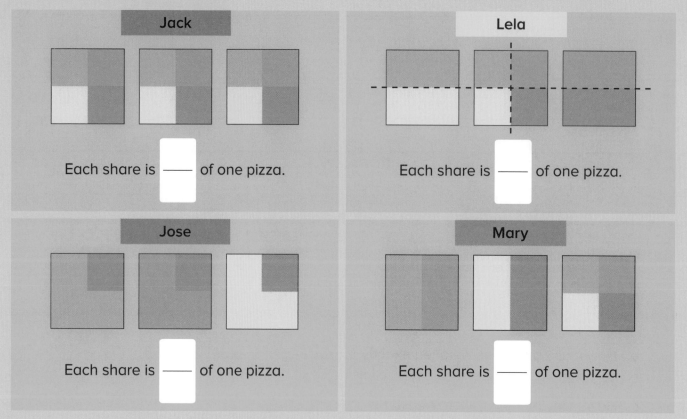

Each share is ⎯ of one pizza.

Each share is ⎯ of one pizza.

Each share is ⎯ of one pizza.

Each share is ⎯ of one pizza.

How much of one whole pizza will be in each share?
Does each person get the same amount?
Does it matter how the pizzas are split?

How many pizzas were shared?

How many people shared the pizza?

How much of one pizza did each person get?

The numerator tells the number of objects to be shared.

The denominator tells the number of shares.

Write the related equation.

☐ ÷ ☐ = ⎯

I. Complete these to show how you would solve each problem.
Color the diagrams to show each share.

a. Two slices of banana bread are shared equally by 3 people.
How much of one whole slice will be in each share?

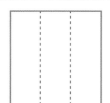 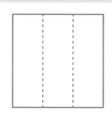

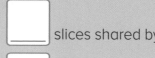 slices shared by

people

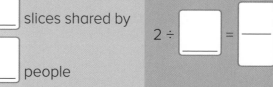 $2 \div \boxed{} = \dfrac{\boxed{}}{\boxed{}}$

b. Three pies are shared equally by 8 people. How much of one whole pie will be in each share?

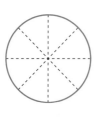

 pies shared by

people

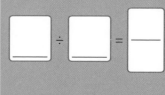 $\boxed{} \div \boxed{} = \dfrac{\boxed{}}{\boxed{}}$

2. Each large rectangle below is one whole. Complete the sentence and color the diagram to show each share.

a. $\dfrac{3}{5}$ is the same as

$\boxed{}$ divided by $\boxed{}$

b. $\dfrac{4}{7}$ is the same as

$\boxed{}$ divided by $\boxed{}$

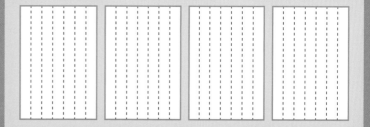

Complete the sentences so that the quotient in the division sentence is the same as the product in the multiplication sentence. Then use the diagram to show why they are the same.

$3 \div 4 = \dfrac{\boxed{}}{\boxed{}}$ $3 \times \dfrac{\boxed{}}{\boxed{}} = \dfrac{\boxed{}}{\boxed{}}$

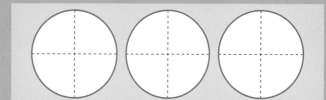

Reinforcing the Relationship Between Fractions and Division

Fractions can be shown in different ways.

Dana drew this diagram to show $\frac{3}{4}$.

How could she shade the circle to show this fraction?

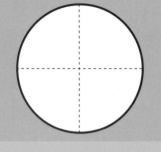

Franco drew and shaded these 3 circles to show $\frac{3}{4}$ another way.

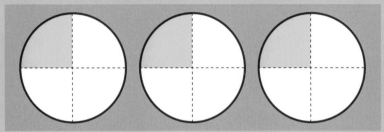

Franco realized that his diagram also showed the equation $3 \div 4 = \boxed{}$.

Do you agree? Why?

What pictures could you draw to show that you are correct?

What numbers would you write to complete this sentence?

$\frac{5}{6}$ is the same as $\boxed{}$ divided by $\boxed{}$.

Step Up

I. Each circle below is one whole. Show each fraction in two different ways. Then complete the sentence.

a.

$\frac{2}{3}$ is the same as $\boxed{}$ divided by $\boxed{}$.

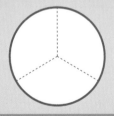 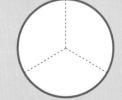 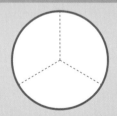

b.

$\frac{3}{5}$ is the same as $\boxed{}$ divided by $\boxed{}$.

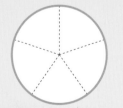 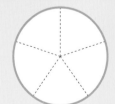 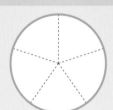 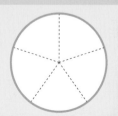

2. Read each incomplete sentence and sketch two different pictures to match.
Then complete the sentence.

a.

$\frac{3}{8}$ is the same as _____ divided by _____.

b.

—— is the same as 3 divided by 12.

3. Solve each problem. Write an equation to show your thinking.

a. Eight people equally shared 3 pizzas. How much pizza did each person eat?

b. Four families equally shared 7 pizzas. How much pizza did each family eat?

Step Ahead

Some friends shared pizzas at a movie night. Each person ate $\frac{1}{3}$ of a pizza. There was no pizza left over.

How many people and how many pizzas would make this story true?
Write three possible solutions.

Dividing a Proper Fraction by a Whole Number (Area Model)

This cake was made for a party.

This picture shows how much cake was left over after the party.
What fraction of the whole cake was left over?

Four families share the remaining cake equally.

What fraction of the original whole cake did each family take home?

How could you figure it out?

I know what fraction is left over. I need to divide that amount into 4 equal parts.

What does this picture show you?

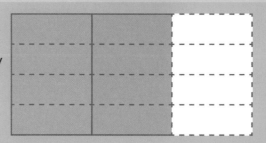

1st family
2nd family
3rd family
4th family

How can the picture help you figure out how much of the original whole cake each family took home?

What equation could you write to show your thinking?

Step Up

1. Each square is one whole. The striped part shows the fraction. Draw more lines and color parts to divide the striped part by the whole number. The first one has been done for you. Then complete the equation.

a.

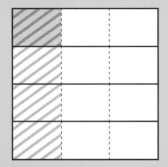

$$\frac{1}{3} \div 4 = \boxed{}$$

b.

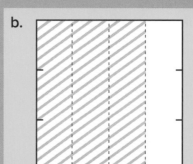

$$\frac{3}{4} \div 3 = \boxed{}$$

2. Complete each of these.

a.

Shade $\frac{2}{5}$

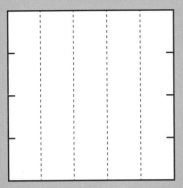

$\frac{2}{5} \div 4 = \boxed{}$

b.

Shade $\frac{5}{8}$

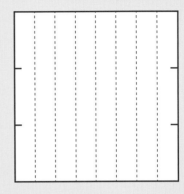

$\frac{5}{8} \div 3 = \boxed{}$

c.

Shade $\frac{5}{6}$

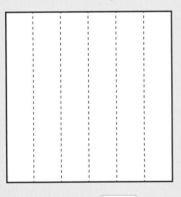

$\frac{5}{6} \div 4 = \boxed{}$

d.

Shade $\frac{3}{5}$

$\frac{3}{5} \div 3 = \boxed{}$

Step Ahead

The shaded part is the result of dividing a fraction by a whole number.
Complete the division equation to match each shaded part.

a.

$\frac{2}{3} \div \boxed{} = \frac{2}{15}$

b.

$\frac{3}{4} \div \boxed{} = \boxed{}$

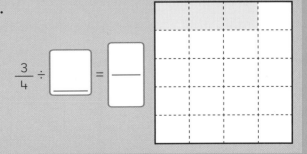

Relating Division of a Unit Fraction to Multiplication

These diagrams were used to figure out $\frac{1}{3}$ divided by 4.

 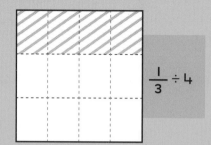 

There is a way to figure out the answers without drawing all the diagrams.

> The last diagram is like multiplying fractions. It is the same as $\frac{1}{3} \times \frac{1}{4}$.

Use these diagrams to help you complete the equations.

 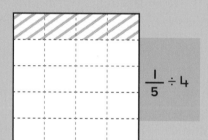 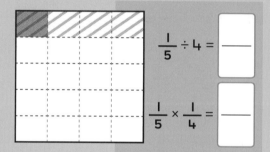

Step Up

I. Each square is one whole. The striped part shows the fraction. Draw more lines and color parts to divide the striped part by the whole number. The first one has been done for you. Then complete the equations.

a.

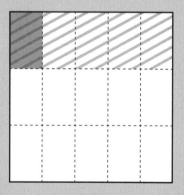

$\frac{1}{3} \div 5 = \boxed{}$ $\frac{1}{3} \times \boxed{} = \boxed{}$

b.

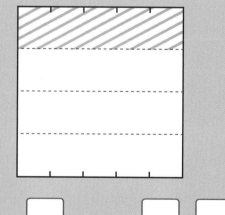

$\frac{1}{4} \div 5 = \boxed{}$ $\frac{1}{4} \times \boxed{} = \boxed{}$

2. Complete each of these.

a.

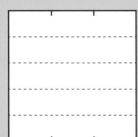

$$\frac{1}{5} \div 3 = \underline{\quad}$$

$$\underline{\quad} \times \underline{\quad} = \underline{\quad}$$

b.

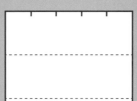

$$\frac{1}{3} \div 5 = \underline{\quad}$$

$$\underline{\quad} \times \underline{\quad} = \underline{\quad}$$

c.

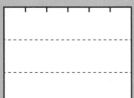

$$\frac{1}{4} \div 6 = \underline{\quad}$$

$$\underline{\quad} \times \underline{\quad} = \underline{\quad}$$

d.

$$\frac{1}{4} \div 4 = \underline{\quad}$$

$$\underline{\quad} \times \underline{\quad} = \underline{\quad}$$

3. For each of these, write the multiplication equation that matches. Then write the answers.

a.

$$\frac{1}{8} \div 6 = \underline{\quad}$$

$$\underline{\quad} \times \underline{\quad} = \underline{\quad}$$

b.

$$\frac{1}{9} \div 2 = \underline{\quad}$$

$$\underline{\quad} \times \underline{\quad} = \underline{\quad}$$

Step Ahead Write two multiplication and two division equations for each shaded region.

a.

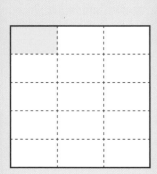

$$\frac{1}{5} \div \underline{\quad} = \underline{\quad}$$

$$\frac{1}{5} \times \underline{\quad} = \underline{\quad}$$

$$\frac{1}{3} \div \underline{\quad} = \underline{\quad}$$

$$\frac{1}{3} \times \underline{\quad} = \underline{\quad}$$

b.

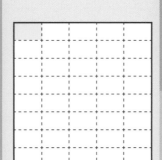

$$\frac{1}{5} \div \underline{\quad} = \underline{\quad}$$

$$\underline{\quad} \times \underline{\quad} = \underline{\quad}$$

$$\frac{1}{8} \div \underline{\quad} = \underline{\quad}$$

$$\underline{\quad} \times \underline{\quad} = \underline{\quad}$$

Solving Word Problems Involving Multiplication or Division of a Unit Fraction

Look at these two word problems.

1 Three people equally shared $\frac{1}{2}$ yd of ribbon to make small bows. How much ribbon is in each share?

2 Each large bow needs $\frac{1}{2}$ yd of ribbon. How much ribbon will be needed to make 3 large bows?

How are they the same? How are they different?

The first problem is starting with a total length and splitting it into equal lengths. That's division.

I could write a division sentence and then change it to a multiplication sentence to find the answer.

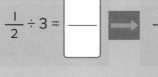

$$\frac{1}{2} \div 3 = \boxed{} \Rightarrow \frac{1}{2} \times \boxed{} = \boxed{}$$

The second problem is combining 3 equal lengths. That's multiplication.

$$\frac{1}{2} \times \boxed{} = \boxed{}$$

What is the solution for each problem?

Step Up Color the ⬤ to show whether the problem is multiplication or division. Then figure out the solution. Show your thinking.

a. Three people share a length of fabric that is $\frac{1}{3}$ yd long. How much fabric is in each share?

◯ Multiplication ◯ Division

_____ yard

b. The length of one side of a square picture frame is $\frac{1}{6}$ yd long. How much wood is needed for the whole picture frame?

◯ Multiplication ◯ Division

_____ yard

c. Four students equally share $\frac{1}{2}$ meter of fabric. How much fabric is in each share?

○ Multiplication   ○ Division

_____ meter

d. A muffin recipe requires $\frac{1}{3}$ of a cup of milk. How much milk is needed to make five batches?

○ Multiplication   ○ Division

_____ cups

e. A team of 3 students ran a relay that was $\frac{1}{2}$ mile in total. Each student ran the same distance. How far did each student run?

○ Multiplication   ○ Division

_____ mile

f. A team of 3 students ran a relay in $\frac{1}{4}$ of an hour. Each student ran for the same amount of time. For how long did each student run?

○ Multiplication   ○ Division

_____ hour

Step Ahead

A team of four people are competing in a relay race that is $8\frac{1}{2}$ miles long. Each person will run the same distance.

a. What distance will each person run? [ ] mi

b. Where should each of the runners be placed along the course to make exchanges?

2nd runner	3rd runner	4th runner
mi	mi	mi

Dividing a Whole Number by a Unit Fraction (Area Model)

Lara's mom is baking 4 large loaves of banana bread.
She will cut each loaf into thirds to sell in separate packages at a bake sale.

Use the diagram above to figure out the number of packages she will make.

How many packages were made?

Why does the answer make sense?

What equations could you write?

$$\boxed{} \times \frac{1}{3} = 4$$

Why do both equations make sense?

$$4 \div \frac{1}{3} = \boxed{}$$

We have to find the number of thirds in 4.

Step Up

1. Each large rectangle below represents one whole. Shade the number of whole shapes. Then draw lines to split each shape into parts to match the fraction. Complete the equations to show the answer.

a. Shade 5 whole shapes.
How many thirds are in 5?

$$\boxed{} \times \frac{1}{3} = 5$$

$$5 \div \frac{1}{3} = \boxed{}$$

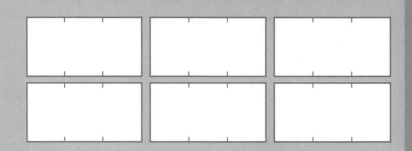

b. Shade 6 whole shapes.
How many fourths are in 6?

$$\boxed{} \times \frac{1}{4} = 6$$

$$6 \div \frac{1}{4} = \boxed{}$$

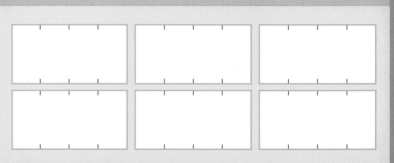

2. Complete these. You can draw lines in the diagram to help.

a. Shade 4 whole shapes.
How many fourths are in 4?

$$\boxed{} \times \frac{1}{4} = 4$$

$$4 \div \frac{1}{4} = \boxed{}$$

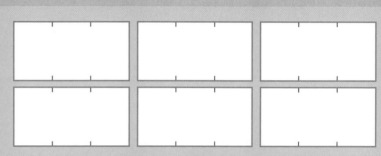

b. Shade 6 whole shapes.
How many thirds are in 6?

$$\boxed{} \times \frac{1}{3} = 6$$

$$6 \div \frac{1}{3} = \boxed{}$$

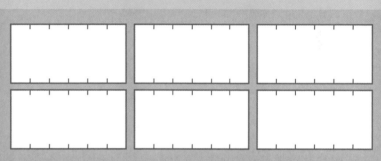

c. Shade 3 whole shapes.
How many sixths are in 3?

$$\boxed{} \times \frac{1}{6} = 3$$

$$3 \div \frac{1}{6} = \boxed{}$$

3. Look at your answers in Question 1 and Question 2. Write what you notice.

Step Ahead

Evan baked some cherry pies. He cut them into 12 equal-sized pieces. What could have been the number of whole pies and the fraction he used to divide the pies? Write equations to show some different possible solutions.

Julia baked 4 large trays of granola bars.
She will cut each tray into thirds to sell in separate packages at a bake sale.

This diagram was used to figure out the number of packages she would make.

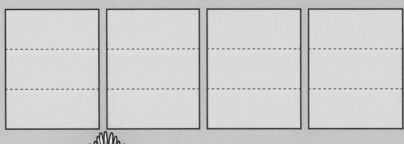

$$4 \div \frac{1}{3} = 12$$

The diagram shows 4 groups of 3 thirds. That's 4 × 3 thirds.

Corey baked 5 large loaves of banana bread and cut each into fourths to sell at the bake sale.

Complete the equations to figure out the number of packages he made.

$$5 \div \frac{1}{4} = \boxed{}$$

$$5 \times \boxed{} = \boxed{}$$

Look at the equations. Why do the answers make sense?

Step Up

1. For each of these, complete the two equations and answer the question. You can draw lines to divide the rectangles into parts. Each large rectangle is one whole.

a.

$$3 \div \frac{1}{4} = \boxed{}$$

$$3 \times \boxed{} = \boxed{}$$

How many fourths in 3?

b.

$$4 \div \frac{1}{5} = \boxed{}$$

$$4 \times \boxed{} = \boxed{}$$

How many fifths in 4?

2. For each of these, complete the equations and answer the question.

a. $5 \div \frac{1}{3} =$ [ ]____ $5 \times$ [ ]____ $=$ [ ]____   How many thirds in 5? [ ]____

b. $6 \div \frac{1}{4} =$ [ ]____ $6 \times$ [ ]____ $=$ [ ]____   How many fourths in 6? [ ]____

c. $3 \div \frac{1}{8} =$ [ ]____ $3 \times$ [ ]____ $=$ [ ]____   How many eighths in 3? [ ]____

d. $4 \div \frac{1}{6} =$ [ ]____ $4 \times$ [ ]____ $=$ [ ]____   How many sixths in 4? [ ]____

e. $2 \div \frac{1}{5} =$ [ ]____ $2 \times$ [ ]____ $=$ [ ]____   How many fifths in 2? [ ]____

3. For each of these, complete the sentences so they describe the same groups.

a.
There are [ ]____ thirds in 2.

[ ]____ $\div \frac{1}{3} =$ [ ]____

2 divided by $\frac{1}{3}$ is [ ]____.

b.
There are [ ]____ fourths in 2.

$2 \div$ [ ]____ $=$ [ ]____

2 divided by [ ]____ is [ ]____.

c.
There are [ ]____ sixths in 3.

[ ]____ $\div \frac{1}{6} =$ [ ]____

[ ]____ divided by $\frac{1}{6}$ is [ ]____.

Step Ahead

Draw a picture to show how to figure out the answer to this equation. Then complete the equation.

$3 \div \frac{1}{3} \div \frac{1}{4} =$ [ ]____

11.8 > Solving Word Problems Involving Unit Fractions

Look at these two word problems.

1 Lora cuts $\frac{1}{2}$ yd of wood into 3 equal lengths. How long is each piece?

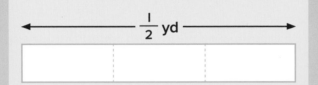

2 How many half-yard lengths of wood can be cut from a piece that is 3 yards long?

How are they the same? How are they different?

> Both problems sound like division.

> The first problem is like sharing among 3.

> The second problem is finding the number of halves in 3 so each of these equations should match one of the problems.

$$\frac{1}{2} \div 3 = \boxed{\phantom{\frac{1}{1}}}$$

$$3 \div \frac{1}{2} = \boxed{}$$

How would you solve each problem?

> Remember, when you divide with fractions, you can change the problem to multiplication if needed.

Step Up ▶ Figure out the solution to each problem. Show your thinking.

a. At a steady pace, it takes $\frac{1}{4}$ hour to walk one kilometer. How far could you walk in 3 hours if you keep the same pace?

_____ km

b. A fast athlete can run 3 kilometers in $\frac{1}{4}$ of an hour. How long does it take the athlete to run one kilometer?

_____ hr

c. A granola recipe requires $\frac{1}{3}$ of a cup of raisins. How many batches can be made with 3 cups of raisins?

_____ batches

d. Half a cup of paint is poured equally into 4 trays. How much paint is in each tray?

_____ cup

e. Every $\frac{1}{6}$ of an hour a factory produces a large car. How many cars are produced in 8 hours?

_____ cars

f. An assembly line produces a new car every 6 minutes. What fraction of an hour is 6 minutes? How many cars are produced in 8 hours?

6 minutes is _____ hour

_____ cars are produced in 8 hours

Step Ahead Gavin can make four flower arrangements every $\frac{1}{4}$ hour. Kayla can make five arrangements every $\frac{1}{3}$ of an hour. Complete this table to compare the number of arrangements that each person makes in 1, 2, 4, 6, and 8 hours.

Hours	1 hour	2 hours	4 hours	6 hours	8 hours
Gavin					
Kayla					

11.9   Converting Between Gallons and Quarts

What amount of liquid is in this container?

It looks like it's halfway between $1\frac{1}{2}$ and 2 gallons.

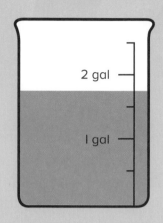

2 gal

1 gal

Imagine the liquid from this container was poured into smaller containers that each held 1 quart. How many of the smaller containers could you fill? How many quarts are in one gallon?

Complete these statements.

☐ quarts	is the same as ➡	**1** gallon.

☐ quarts	is the same as ➡	$\frac{1}{2}$ gallon	**or**	**0.5** gallon.

☐ quart	is the same as ➡	$\frac{1}{4}$ gallon	**or**	**0.25** gallon.

☐ quarts	is the same as ➡	$\frac{3}{4}$ gallon	**or**	**0.75** gallon.

How could you use the statements to figure out the number of quarts in 3.5 gallons?

What number sentence would you write?

Step Up ➡   1.   Convert each amount to quarts.

a.
5 gal = ☐ qt

b.
3 gal = ☐ qt

c.
6 gal = ☐ qt

d.
15 gal = ☐ qt

e.
8.25 gal = ☐ qt

f.
12.5 gal = ☐ qt

g.
4.75 gal = ☐ qt

h.
7.5 gal = ☐ qt

i.
6.25 gal = ☐ qt

2. Convert each amount to gallons.

a. [ ] gal = 8 qt

b. [ ] gal = 32 qt

c. [ ] gal = 24 qt

d. [ ] gal = 10 qt

e. [ ] gal = 21 qt

f. [ ] gal = 15 qt

g. [ ] gal = 1 qt

h. [ ] gal = 40 qt

i. [ ] gal = 3 qt

3. Write the missing amount so that each balance picture is true.

a.
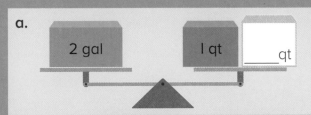
2 gal   1 qt ____ qt

b.

____ qt 8 qt   3 gal

c.
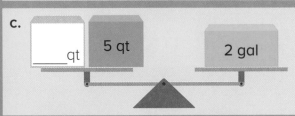
____ qt 5 qt   2 gal

d.
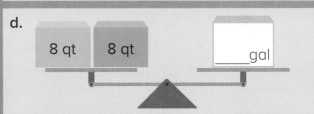
8 qt 8 qt   ____ gal

e.
2.5 gal   6 qt ____ qt

f.
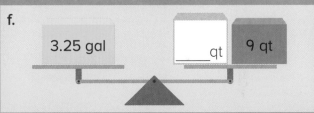
3.25 gal   ____ qt 9 qt

Step Ahead Look at the price for the quart of milk. Write a price that you think is fair for the bottle of milk. Explain your thinking.

_____

_____

_____

_____

$1.90

MILK
1 quart

$ _____

MILK
1 gallon

© ORIGO Education.

11.10 ▶ Converting Between Quarts and Fluid Ounces

Imagine this pitcher is used to fill the empty bottles with water.

How many bottles can be filled from one full pitcher?

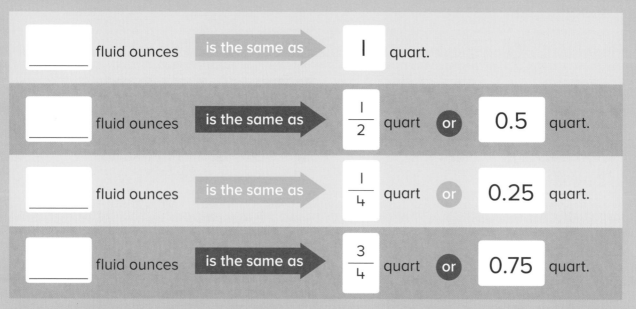

I know there are 32 fl oz in 1 quart.

How many pitchers of water are needed to fill six of these bottles?

Complete these statements.

_____ fluid ounces	is the same as	**1** quart.
_____ fluid ounces	is the same as	$\frac{1}{2}$ quart **or** **0.5** quart.
_____ fluid ounces	is the same as	$\frac{1}{4}$ quart **or** **0.25** quart.
_____ fluid ounces	is the same as	$\frac{3}{4}$ quart **or** **0.75** quart.

How could you use the statements to figure out the number of fluid ounces in 3 quarts?

What number sentence would you write?

Step Up ▶

1. In each pair, draw a ✔ on the container that will hold **more** water.

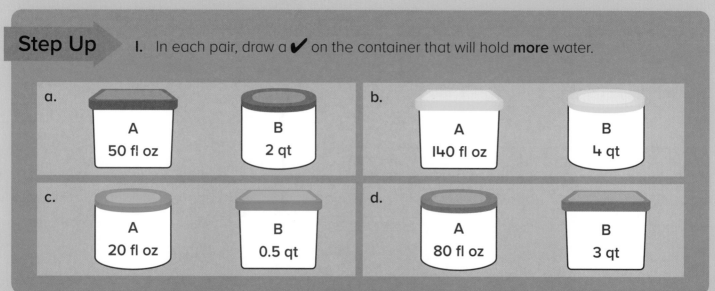

a.
A 50 fl oz   B 2 qt

b.
A 140 fl oz   B 4 qt

c.
A 20 fl oz   B 0.5 qt

d.
A 80 fl oz   B 3 qt

2. Convert each amount to fluid ounces. Write number sentences to show your thinking.

a.

5 qt = [　　　] fl oz

b.

4.75 qt = [　　　] fl oz

c.

3.5 qt = [　　　] fl oz

d.

6.25 qt = [　　　] fl oz

3. Color the ⬭ beside your estimate.

a. 48 fl oz	**b.** 176 fl oz	**c.** 128 fl oz	**d.** 96 fl oz
is closest to	**is closest to**	**is closest to**	**is closest to**
⬭ 2 qt	⬭ 3.5 qt	⬭ 4 qt	⬭ 2.5 qt
⬭ 1 qt	⬭ 6 qt	⬭ 3 qt	⬭ 3 qt
⬭ 1.5 qt	⬭ 4 qt	⬭ 5.5 qt	⬭ 3.5 qt
⬭ 2.5 qt	⬭ 5.5 qt	⬭ 2.5 qt	⬭ 1.5 qt

Step Ahead ➤ Write the missing amount so that each balance picture is true.

a.

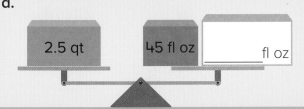

2.5 qt　　45 fl oz　　[　　] fl oz

b.

[　　] fl oz　　50 fl oz　　[　　] fl oz　　2 qt

A water cooler that holds $2\frac{1}{2}$ gallons is placed at a drink station at a fun run. Cups that each hold 8 fl oz are also provided. There are 50 participants in the race.

Has enough water been provided for each person to have one cup?

Each cup holds 8 fl oz, so 4 cups is equal to one quart. There are 4 quarts in a gallon.

How much water should be provided?

Complete these statements.

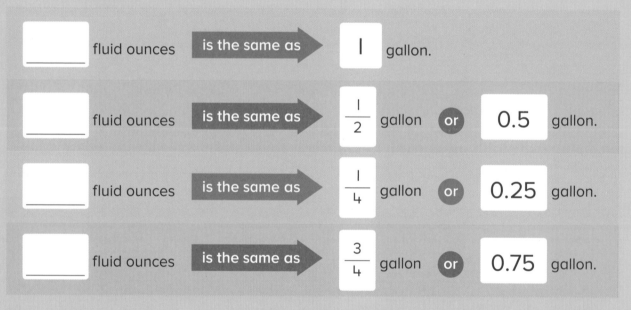

☐ fluid ounces	**is the same as** ▶	1 gallon.
☐ fluid ounces	**is the same as** ▶	$\frac{1}{2}$ gallon **or** 0.5 gallon.
☐ fluid ounces	**is the same as** ▶	$\frac{1}{4}$ gallon **or** 0.25 gallon.
☐ fluid ounces	**is the same as** ▶	$\frac{3}{4}$ gallon **or** 0.75 gallon.

How could you use the statements to figure out the number of fluid ounces in 4.5 gallons?

What number sentence would you write?

Step Up ▶ 1. In each pair, draw a ✔ on the container that will hold **more** water.

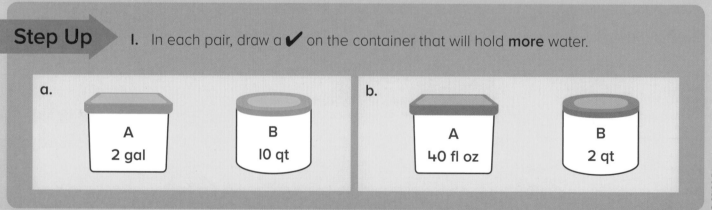

a.
A — 2 gal   B — 10 qt

b.
A — 40 fl oz   B — 2 qt

2. Convert each amount to fluid ounces. Write number sentences to show your thinking.

a.

5 gal = _____ fl oz

b.

3 gal = _____ fl oz

c.

1.5 gal = _____ fl oz

d.

3.25 gal = _____ fl oz

3. Color the ⬭ beside your estimate.

a. 250 fl oz	**b.** 570 fl oz	**c.** 310 fl oz	**d.** 170 fl oz
is closest to	**is closest to**	**is closest to**	**is closest to**
⚪ 2 gal	⚪ 5.5 gal	⚪ 5 gal	⚪ 2.75 gal
⚪ 3 gal	⚪ 4.5 gal	⚪ 5.5 gal	⚪ 1.25 gal
⚪ 1.5 gal	⚪ 2 gal	⚪ 3 gal	⚪ 1 gal
⚪ 1 gal	⚪ 7 gal	⚪ 2.5 gal	⚪ 3 gal

Step Ahead ➤ Imagine the liquid from each full small container was poured into the empty large container. Mark the scale on the large container to show the amount of liquid that will be in the container.

A — 0.75 gal

B — 1 qt

C — 32 fl oz

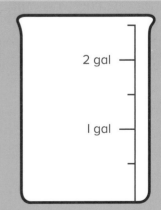

2 gal

1 gal

Solving Word Problems Involving Conversions of Liquid Volume (Capacity)

Logan buys a 2.5-gal bottle of water each time he does the shopping. He uses the water to fill these drink bottles for his family each day.

How many days would each 2.5-gal bottle of water last? How do you know?

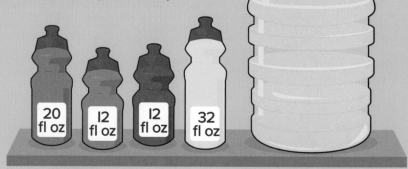

First, I need to figure out the total amount of water that is used each day.

How many fluid ounces are in 2.5 gallons?

If his family only used drink bottles that each held 32 fl oz, how many of those could Logan fill from the 2.5 gal bottle of water? How do you know?

I know that 32 fl oz is the same as 1 quart. How many quarts in 2.5 gallons?

If each small bottle held 12 fl oz, how many could be filled?

If each small bottle held 20 fl oz, how many could be filled?

Step Up

1. Use the pictures at the top of this page to solve these problems. Show your thinking.

a. The 2.5 gallons of water is used to fill the four different drink bottles once each day. How much water is used in two days?	b. The 2.5 gallons of water is used to fill the 4 different drink bottles once a day for 3 days. How much water is left in the large container?
_____ fl oz	_____ fl oz

2. Solve these problems. Show your thinking.

a. Olivia has a quart of milk in the fridge and another half a gallon of milk in the freezer. How much milk does she have in total?

_____ gal

b. Container A holds 9 qt. Container B holds 260 fl oz. Container C holds 2.5 gal. What is the difference between the amounts Containers B and C hold?

_____ fl oz

c. Jamal opens a 2-gal bottle of water. He pours 4 full glasses of water. Each glass holds 8 fl oz. How much water is left in the bottle?

_____ gal

d. A storekeeper is running low on milk. He counts 4 two-gallon bottles, 3 half-gallon cartons, and 6 quarts. How many gallons of milk does he have in total?

_____ gal

Step Ahead

Noah buys five bottles of juice for a party. Each bottle holds 59 fl oz. He pours them all into one large bowl to make fruit punch.

At least how many gallons must the bowl hold? _____ gal

Working Space

12.1 Dividing Decimal Fractions by Whole Numbers

This pitcher holds 0.8 quarts of juice.
Imagine four people share the juice equally.

How much juice will each person have?

What operation will you use to figure out the answer?

What expression could you write to show the problem?

It helps me to remember that 0.8 is a fraction.

0.8 shared by 4 is the same as 8 tenths shared by 4.

This is like an unknown factor problem.

4 × ? = 0.8

Five flags are positioned at equal distances around the inside of an athletics track that is 0.25 miles long.

If you walk around the inside of track, how far is it between each pair of flags?

I would think 25 hundredths divided by 5. It's easy then because 25 ÷ 5 = 5.

What is the distance?

Step Up

1. Rewrite each decimal fraction as a number of tenths or hundredths.

a. 0.24

is the same as

24 hundredths

b. 0.6

is the same as

_____

c. 0.05

is the same as

_____

2. Solve each problem. Show your thinking.

a. Isabelle uses 0.6 kg of dog food to feed her 3 dogs. How much food will she give each dog?

_____ kg

b. A piece of lumber is marked into 9 equal lengths. Three lengths are cut off. The leftover piece is 0.48 meters long. How long is each marked piece?

_____ m

3. Complete each equation. Remember to write the quotient as a decimal fraction. Show your thinking.

a. 0.9 ÷ 3 = 0.3

b. 0.8 ÷ 4 = _____

c. 0.36 ÷ 9 = _____

d. 0.45 ÷ 5 = _____

e. 0.06 ÷ 3 = _____

f. 0.4 ÷ 2 = _____

g. 0.60 ÷ 30 = _____

h. 0.80 ÷ 20 = _____

i. 0.01 ÷ 1 = _____

Step Ahead

1. Three coins have a total value of $0.30.

a. What is the value of each coin? _____

b. What fraction of a dollar is each coin worth?

c. Complete this equation to show your thinking. $0.30 ÷ 3 = $ _____

2. Four coins have a total value of $0.20. Complete this equation to show what each coin is worth. $ _____ ÷ _____ = $ _____

12.2 ▶ Using Partial Quotients with Decimal Fractions

How can you split the cost of this meal equally among four people?

You could break $24.20 into dollars and cents. This diagram makes the division easier.

How much is each person's share?

What fraction of one dollar is one cent?

How would you write that as a decimal fraction?

What fraction of one dollar is five cents?

How would you write that as a decimal fraction?

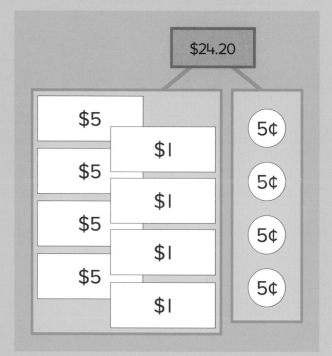

$24.20

$5	$1	5¢
$5	$1	5¢
$5	$1	5¢
$5	$1	5¢

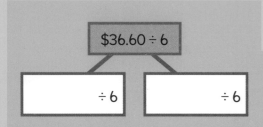

$36.60 ÷ 6

| ÷ 6 | ÷ 6 |

Complete this diagram to show how you could break up $36.60 to divide by 6.

What is the answer?

Step Up   I.   Complete the parts and then write the answer.

a. $8.60 ÷ 4 is the same as $_____ ÷ 4 plus _____ ¢ ÷ 4 = $_____

b. $15.50 ÷ 5 is the same as $_____ ÷ 5 plus _____ ¢ ÷ 5 = $_____

c. $12.90 ÷ 6 is the same as $_____ ÷ 6 plus _____ ¢ ÷ 6 = $_____

d. $18.60 ÷ 3 is the same as $_____ ÷ 3 plus _____ ¢ ÷ 3 = $_____

2. Figure out each share and complete the number sentences.

a.

Share  $63.60 by 3.

$ _63_ ÷ _3_ = $ _____

_60_ ¢ ÷ _3_ = _____ ¢

Each share is

$ _____

b.

Share $32.80 by 4.

$ _____ ÷ _____ = $ _____

_____ ¢ ÷ _____ = _____ ¢

Each share is

$ _____

c.

Share $54.60 by 6.

$ _____ ÷ _____ = $ _____

_____ ¢ ÷ _____ = _____ ¢

Each share is

$ _____

3. Complete each equation. Show your thinking.

a.
12.60 ÷ 3 = _____

b.
48.60 ÷ 2 = _____

c.
36.60 ÷ 3 = _____

d.
28.08 ÷ 4 = _____

e.
50.10 ÷ 5 = _____

f.
16.20 ÷ 4 = _____

Step Ahead

Three friends decide to contribute equal amounts to buy a surfboard. How much **less** will they each have to pay if a fourth person contributes?

$ _____ less

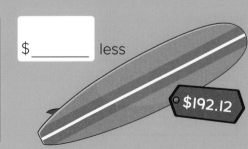

$192.12

Extending the Partial-Quotients Strategy with Decimal Fractions

Six students equally share the cost of this gift.
How much will they each pay?

$45.60

I can split $45.60 into two
parts that are easier to divide.

How many of the whole dollars can be shared by 6?
How much remains to be shared?

$45.60

[ ] + [ ]

Complete this diagram to show how you would
split $45.60 into two parts that are easier to divide by 6.

Is there another way you could divide?

Step Up

1. Break each number into parts that you can easily divide. Calculate the partial
quotients. Then complete the equations.

a.
$22.50 ÷ 3 = $ _____

___ ÷ 3 = ___   ___ ÷ 3 = ___

b.
$34.40 ÷ 8 = $ _____

___ ÷ 8 = ___   ___ ÷ 8 = ___

c.
$27.60 ÷ 6 = $ _____

___ ÷ 6 = ___   ___ ÷ 6 = ___

d.
$28.80 ÷ 9 = $ _____

___ ÷ 9 = ___   ___ ÷ 9 = ___

e.
$52.80 ÷ 8 = $ _____

___ ÷ 8 = ___   ___ ÷ 8 = ___

f.
$34.80 ÷ 4 = $ _____

___ ÷ 4 = ___   ___ ÷ 4 = ___

2. Calculate the quotients. Show your thinking.

a. $44.70 \div 3 =$ _____

b. $37.60 \div 4 =$ _____

c. $48.60 \div 9 =$ _____

d. $37.10 \div 7 =$ _____

e. $25.20 \div 3 =$ _____

f. $14.40 \div 4 =$ _____

g. $58.40 \div 8 =$ _____

h. $39.60 \div 6 =$ _____

i. $46.90 \div 7 =$ _____

Step Ahead

Four students each contributed $8.40 to buy a gift for their teacher. Then three more students decided to contribute toward the same gift. How much will each student have to pay now?

$ _____

Working Space

12.4 ▶ Dividing Whole Numbers by Decimal Fractions

Each large square represents one whole.

How many equal parts are in each whole?

How many tenths are in two wholes?

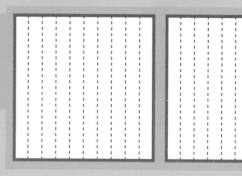

How would you write this as a division equation?

Write an equation using a common fraction.
Then write an equation using a decimal fraction.

$$\boxed{} \div \boxed{\frac{}{}} = \boxed{} \qquad \boxed{} \div \boxed{0.} = \boxed{}$$

Look at these two wholes.

How many equal parts are in each whole?

Shade 5 tenths of one whole.

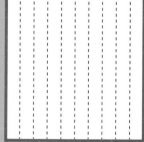

How many times can you shade 5 tenths so that both squares are completely shaded?

Think of equations you could write to show this.
Use common and decimal fractions.

Felix thought of these two different stories to help him figure out the equations.

Story A	Story B
There are 2 loaves of garlic bread, cut into tenths.	There are 2 loaves of garlic bread, cut into tenths.
If each person takes 5 pieces that means 4 people have bread.	If 4 people share it equally that means each person gets 5 tenths.

What equations can you write to match each story?

Story A   Story B

$$\boxed{} \div \boxed{} = \boxed{} \qquad \boxed{} \div \boxed{} = \boxed{}$$

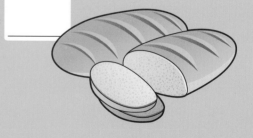

What is the same about each equation?

What is different?

How are they related?

Step Up

1. Each large square represents one whole. Figure out how many tenths or hundredths are in each shaded section, and how many sections are needed to cover the square completely. Then complete the equations.

a.

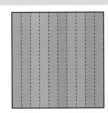

$1 \div \dfrac{2}{10} = 5$

$\boxed{} \div 0.\underline{} = \boxed{}$

b.

$\boxed{} \div \dfrac{}{10} = \boxed{}$

$\boxed{} \div 0.\underline{} = \boxed{}$

c.

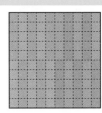

$\boxed{} \div \dfrac{}{100} = \boxed{}$

$\boxed{} \div 0.0\underline{} = \boxed{}$

2. Each large square represents one whole. Shade or outline parts to help you figure out the quotients. Then complete the equations.

a.

$2 \div 0.4 = \boxed{}$

b.

$2 \div 0.08 = \boxed{}$

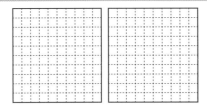

c.

$2 \div 0.5 = \boxed{}$

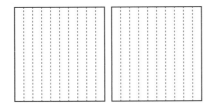

d.

$2 \div 0.40 = \boxed{}$

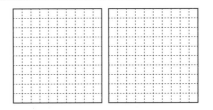

Step Ahead

Figure out a way of splitting these four wholes into equal groups of tenths. Complete the equation.

$4 \div \dfrac{}{10} = \boxed{}$

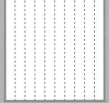

12.5   Using Multiplication to Help Divide by Decimal Fractions

Three pitchers each hold a liter of juice.

Some small cups each hold one-tenth of a liter.

How many of these cups could be filled to use all the juice?

What operation will you use to figure out the answer?

What expression could you write to show the problem?

I could use division to figure out the number of cups.
$3 ÷ 0.1 = ?$

I could also "think multiplication".
$? × 0.1 = 3$

You could start by thinking
$? × 0.1 = 1$

Some larger cups each hold two-tenths of liter.

How many of these cups could be filled to use all the juice?

Emma drew this diagram to help.

$3 ÷ 0.2 = \underline{}$

$× 3$ ⑤ $× 0.2 =$ ① $× 3$

⑮ $× 0.2 =$ ③

How do you think the diagram helps?

Which number in the last equation tells you how many cups would be needed?

a.

$4 ÷ 0.5 = \boxed{}$

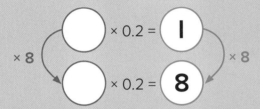

$2 × 0.5 = 1$

$× 4$ $× 4$

$ × 0.5 = 4$

b.

$5 ÷ 0.1 = \boxed{}$

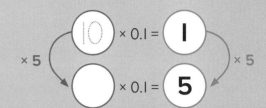

$10 × 0.1 = 1$

$× 5$ $× 5$

$ × 0.1 = 5$

c.

$8 ÷ 0.2 = \boxed{}$

$ × 0.2 = 1$

$× 8$ $× 8$

$ × 0.2 = 8$

d.

$4 ÷ 0.05 = \boxed{}$

$ × 0.05 = 1$

$× 4$ $× 4$

$ × 0.05 = 4$

e.

$6 ÷ 0.4 = \boxed{}$

$ × 0.4 = 2$

$× 3$ $× 3$

$ × 0.4 = 6$

f.

$3 ÷ 0.25 = \boxed{}$

$ × 0.25 = 1$

$× 3$ $× 3$

$ × 0.25 = 3$

Step Ahead

Amber bought a 6-meter roll of ribbon. She needs pieces that are 20 centimeters long. How many pieces will she be able to cut from the roll? Show your thinking.

_____ pieces

Exploring Multiplication and Division Involving Decimal Fractions

Look at these equations. What do you know about the answers?

$4 \times 0.1 =$ ___

$4 \times 0.01 =$ ___

$4 \div 0.1 =$ ___

$4 \div 0.01 =$ ___

Which equations will have an answer that is greater than 4? Which will be less than 4?

Which equation will have the greatest answer? Which one will have the least? How do you know?

How are these problems the same? How are they different?

Deon is planning a camping trip. He will take 10 gallons of drinking water. If he uses about 0.5 gal of water each day, how long will the water last?

Mato is planning a camping trip. He plans to be away for 10 days. If he uses about 0.5 gal of water each day, how much water will he need to take?

What steps would you use to figure out the answer to each problem?

What equation would you write to solve each problem?

Which answer will be greater? How do you know?

Step Up

1. In each pair, loop the expression that will have the **greater** answer. Show your thinking.

a.

8×0.5 **or** $8 \div 0.5$

b.

8×0.5 **or** 8×0.05

c.

8×0.05 **or** $8 \div 0.05$

d.

$8 \div 0.5$ **or** $8 \div 0.05$

2. Write an equation to show how you would solve each problem.
Then use a method of your choice to figure out the answer.

a. James is cutting 9 pieces of fabric that are each 0.7 yd long. What is the total length of fabric he needs?

_____ yd

b. A water pipe loses 2 gallons of water every minute. How long will it take to lose 20 gallons of water?

_____ min

c. A newborn calf gains about 0.8 kg each day. How many days will it take to gain 24 kg?

_____ days

d. A large egg weighs about 0.06 kg. What will be the total weight of 8 large eggs?

_____ kg

Step Ahead ▶ Complete this trail.

1.5 → × 4 → ☐ → ÷ 0.6 → ☐

☐ ← − 0.1 ← ☐ ← ÷ 4 ← ☐ ← + 0.36 ←

Comparing Multiplication and Division Involving Decimal Fractions

What word problem involving 2 loaves of banana bread could you write to match each of these equations?

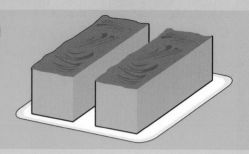

$2 \div 10 =$ ___

$2 \div 1 =$ ___

$2 \div 0.1 =$ ___

$2 \div 0.01 =$ ___

How could you figure out the answers?

Write the answers in this place-value chart.

What do you notice?

Why does it make sense that dividing by 0.01 has the greatest quotient?

	H	T	O	.	t
$2 \div 10 =$				.	
$2 \div 1 =$				.	
$2 \div 0.1 =$				.	
$2 \div 0.01 =$				.	

Step Up

1. Use a pattern to help you write the answers in the place-value charts below.

Multiplication

a.

	Th	H	T	O	.	t	h
$40 \times 10 =$					.		
$40 \times 1 =$					.		
$40 \times 0.1 =$					.		
$40 \times 0.01 =$					.		

Division

b.

	Th	H	T	O	.	t	h
$40 \div 10 =$					.		
$40 \div 1 =$					.		
$40 \div 0.1 =$					.		
$40 \div 0.01 =$					.		

c.

	Th	H	T	O	.	t	h
$60 \times 10 =$					.		
$60 \times 1 =$					.		
$60 \times 0.1 =$					.		
$60 \times 0.01 =$					.		

d.

	Th	H	T	O	.	t	h
$60 \div 10 =$					.		
$60 \div 1 =$					.		
$60 \div 0.1 =$					.		
$60 \div 0.01 =$					.		

2. Write the answers in these place-value charts.

Multiplication

a.

	Th	H	T	O	t	h
80 × 20 =					•	
80 × 2 =					•	
80 × 0.2 =					•	
80 × 0.02 =					•	

Division

b.

	Th	H	T	O	t	h
80 ÷ 20 =					•	
80 ÷ 2 =					•	
80 ÷ 0.2 =					•	
80 ÷ 0.02 =					•	

3. a. Look at the multiplication chart above. What do you notice when one factor decreases?

_____

_____

_____

b. Look at the division chart above. What do you notice when one factor decreases?

_____

_____

_____

Step Ahead

Color **blue** the expressions that equal 300.
Color **red** the expressions that equal 30.

1,200 ÷ 4	120 ÷ 0.4	12 ÷ 0.4	120 ÷ 0.04

120 ÷ 4	1,200 ÷ 40	120 ÷ 40	12 ÷ 4

Working Space

Renaming Decimal Fractions to Divide
(Whole Numbers by Tenths)

Jacob made two pies for his family.
Each pie was cut into tenths.

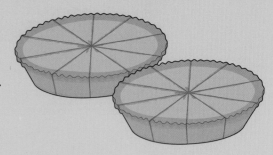

Each person ate two pieces of pie and there were no leftovers.
How many people are in Jacob's family?

Eva realized that the two pies had a total of 20 tenths.
Complete this statement to show her thinking.

$2 \div 0.2$ **has the same answer as** $20 \div 2 =$ ☐

Describe Eva's thinking.

Use her thinking to complete this statement.

$2 \div 0.4$ **has the same answer as** $20 \div$ ☐ $=$ ☐

Step Up   I. Complete these statements.

a. $8 \div 0.2$

is the same as

_____ tenths ÷ _____ tenths

which is the same as

$80 \div$ _____ $=$ _____

b. $7 \div 0.5$

is the same as

_____ tenths ÷ _____ tenths

which is the same as

$70 \div$ _____ $=$ _____

c. $6 \div 0.4$

is the same as

_____ tenths ÷ _____ tenths

which is the same as

$60 \div$ _____ $=$ _____

d. $4 \div 0.8$

is the same as

_____ tenths ÷ _____ tenths

which is the same as

$40 \div$ _____ $=$ _____

e. $12 \div 0.3$

is the same as

_____ tenths ÷ _____ tenths

which is the same as

$120 \div$ _____ $=$ _____

f. $9 \div 0.6$

is the same as

_____ tenths ÷ _____ tenths

which is the same as

$90 \div$ _____ $=$ _____

2. Complete the parts to match.

a.

$5 \div 0.2$ | 50 tenths ÷ ___ tenths | ___ ÷ ___ = ___

b.

$9 \div 0.3$ | ___ tenths ÷ ___ tenths | ___ ÷ ___ = ___

c.

$12 \div 0.5$ | ___ tenths ÷ ___ tenths | ___ ÷ ___ = ___

3. Solve these problems. Use a method of your choice. Show your thinking.

a. Maka can walk 0.3 km in one minute. If she continues to walk at the same speed, how long will it take her to walk 6 km?

_____ minutes

b. One load of laundry uses 0.2 liters of liquid detergent. How many loads could be done from a 3-liter bottle of detergent?

_____ loads

c. An athlete needs to lose 12 kg. If he can lose 0.2 kg a day, how long will it take him to lose the weight?

_____ days

d. Chang's motorcycle uses about 0.6 gallons of gas each day. Approximately how long will 9 gallons last?

_____ days

Step Ahead Follow the steps and write the answers along this trail.

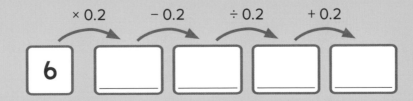

× 0.2   − 0.2   ÷ 0.2   + 0.2

6   ___   ___   ___   ___

12.9 Renaming Decimal Fractions to Divide (Tenths by Tenths)

Layla has a ribbon that is 2.4 meters long.
She needs to cut the ribbon into lengths of 0.3 meters to make bows.

How many bows can she make?

We know we are dividing by 3 tenths.
We also know 2.4 m is 24 tenths.

It is much easier to divide by a whole number. If possible, rewrite the problem so the divisor is not a decimal fraction.

Complete this statement to calculate the answer.

2.4 ÷ 0.3	has the same answer as	24 ÷ 3 = _____

How would you figure out the quotient for this example?

$$0.8 ÷ 0.2 = ?$$

Complete this statement to help figure it out.

| 0.8 ÷ 0.2 | _____ tenths ÷ _____ tenths | _____ ÷ _____ = _____ |

Step Up   I. Write the missing numbers so the statements are true.

a.
| 0.9 ÷ 0.3 | _____ tenths ÷ _____ tenths | _____ ÷ _____ = _____ |

b.
| 0.6 ÷ 0.2 | _____ tenths ÷ _____ tenths | _____ ÷ _____ = _____ |

c.
| 7.2 ÷ 0.6 | _____ tenths ÷ _____ tenths | _____ ÷ _____ = _____ |

d.
| 3.2 ÷ 0.4 | _____ tenths ÷ _____ tenths | _____ ÷ _____ = _____ |

e.
| 4.5 ÷ 0.3 | _____ tenths ÷ _____ tenths | _____ ÷ _____ = _____ |

2. Solve each problem. Show your thinking.

a. Mia can run 0.3 km in one minute. How long will it take her to run 4.5 km?

_____ minutes

b. Daniel uses 0.6 kilogram of sand for every batch of concrete. How many batches can he make from 30 kilograms of sand?

_____ batches

c. A pool needs 0.4 gallons of softener every day. How many days will a 6.4-gallon container last?

_____ days

d. Alisa needs 0.6 yards of fabric to make each curtain panel. How many panels can she make from 7.2 yards of fabric?

_____ panels

Step Ahead

a. Follow the steps and write the answers along this trail.

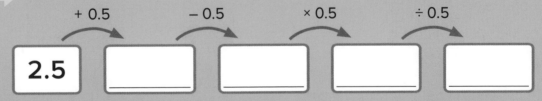

b. Write a different operation for each part in this trail so the final answer is **greater than** the final answer in the trail above.

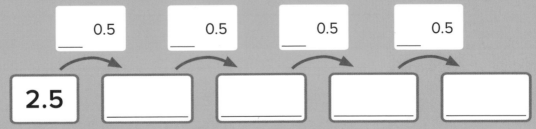

How much juice is in this pitcher?

Imagine the juice was poured into smaller containers that each held 200 mL. How many of the smaller containers could you fill? How many milliliters are in one liter?

Complete these statements.

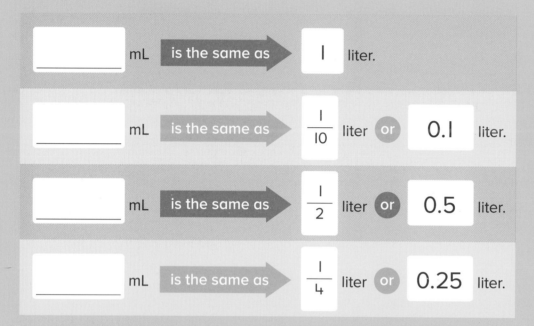

_____ mL **is the same as** ⟶ 1 liter.

_____ mL **is the same as** ⟶ $\frac{1}{10}$ liter **or** 0.1 liter.

_____ mL **is the same as** ⟶ $\frac{1}{2}$ liter **or** 0.5 liter.

_____ mL **is the same as** ⟶ $\frac{1}{4}$ liter **or** 0.25 liter.

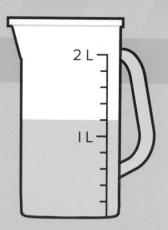

Step Up

1. Write the amount in each container in three different ways.

Whole number	mL	mL	mL
Common fraction	L	L	L
Decimal fraction	L	L	L

2. Color the three labels that match each amount.

a.

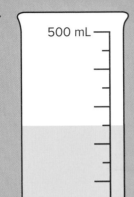

2.5 L

| 250 mL |

| $\frac{1}{4}$ L |

| 0.25 L |

b.

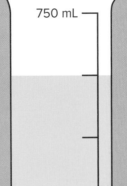

0.5 L

| $\frac{1}{2}$ L |

| 500 mL |

| 5,000 mL |

c.

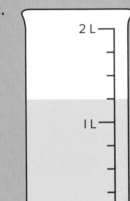

$1\frac{1}{4}$ L

| 1.25 L |

| 1,250 mL |

| 125 mL |

d.

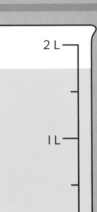

750 mL

| 1.75 L |

| 1,750 mL |

| $1\frac{3}{4}$ L |

Step Ahead

Write two ways you could fill this container to the 2-L mark using these two measuring cups.

Method A

_____

_____

Method B

_____

_____

Adding Mixed Units of Liquid Volume (Capacity)

Imagine you poured all the liquid from these two full pitchers into one container.

How could you figure out the combined volume of the liquid?

What is another way you could describe the total amount of liquid?

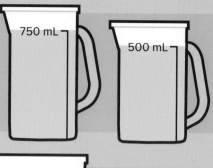

Imagine you poured all the liquid from these two full pitchers into one container.

What do you need to do before you can figure out the combined liquid volume?

Which amount would you convert?

When you convert a number of liters to a number of milliliters, does the total volume change?

What part changes? Why?

Step Up

These students each had three different bottles of water.
Use this information to answer Questions 1 to 5 on pages 292 and 293.

Lilly	Akari	Carter	Ramon
A　　2 L	**A**　375 mL	**A**　　1.25 L	**A**　　　1 L
B　450 mL	**B**　　1.5 L	**B**　250 mL	**B**　700 mL
C　　1.2 L	**C**　600 mL	**C**　　　3 L	**C**　　2.5 L
Total ____ ? ____	Total ____ ? ____	Total ____ ? ____	Total ____ ? ____

1. What do the students need to do before they can calculate their total amount of water?

_____

_____

2. Figure out the total amount of water that each student has.
Write your answers in liters and milliliters.

Lilly	Akari	Carter	Ramon
_____ L	_____ L	_____ L	_____ L
_____ mL	_____ mL	_____ mL	_____ mL

Working Space

Look at the totals in Question 2.

3. a. Who had the **greatest** amount of water? _____

   b. Who had the **least** amount of water? _____

4. Whose total amount was closest to each of these?

   a. $3\frac{1}{2}$ liters _____

   b. $4\frac{1}{4}$ liters _____

5. Draw a ✔ on the student totals that you could figure out mentally.

Step Ahead   Write number sentences to show how you add to find five different totals using three or more of these containers.

a. _____

b. _____

c. _____

d. _____

e. _____

250 mL
2 L

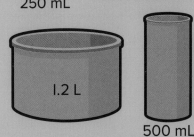
1.2 L
500 mL

Trina is shopping for some party supplies. There are 20 people attending.

Which bottle of water should she buy? Which disposable cups could she buy? How did you decide?

Trina wants to provide at least one cup of water for each person.

If she uses the 250-mL cups, how many bottles of water should she buy?

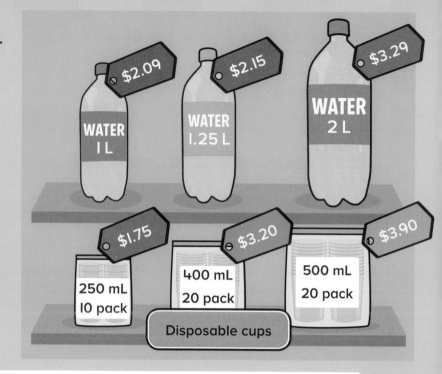

I will call the total amount of water **W**. W = 20 × 250 mL which is the same as W = 5 × (4 × 250 mL). That's 5,000 mL or 5 liters.

What is the total cost of this purchase?

Step Up

1. Use the pictures at the top of the page to solve these problems.

a.	Rita buys three 1-L bottles of water and one pack of medium-sized cups. How many whole cups can she fill?	b.	Cole buys four 1.25-L bottles of water and one pack of large cups. How many cups can he fill?

_____ cups

_____ cups

2. Solve these word problems. Show your thinking.

a. Zoe buys 1.5 L of juice. She pours two full glasses. Each glass holds 400 mL. What amount is left in the bottle?

_____ mL

b. Megan cleans up after her party and counts three 1.25-L bottles of water that are half full. How much water is left over?

_____ mL

c. Juan pours 2 L of water equally into 10 cups. Each cup holds 400 mL. There is no water left in the bottle. How much water is in each cup?

_____ mL

d. Dixon buys 2 L of juice and six 375-mL cans of soda water. He pours the juice and water into one large bowl to make punch. How much punch did he make?

_____ mL

Step Ahead   Loop the special that you think is the better buy. Explain your thinking.

_____

_____

INDEX